READING CARAVAN

Peacock
Lane

Paul A. Witty
Professor of Education, Northwestern University

Alma Moore Freeland
Associate Professor of Elementary Education
University of Texas

D. C. HEATH AND COMPANY
BOSTON

Contributing Authors

Charlotte Thompson, *Teacher, Tyler Public Schools, Tyler, Texas*
Mae Moore Campbell, *Teacher, Marshall Public Schools, Marshall, Texas*

Illustrators

Winnie Fitch Phelan: cover and pages 11, 47, 61, 99, 159, 213, 257, 283.
Don Madden: pages 12–20, 49–58, 97.
Ati Forberg: pages 21, 40–44, 160–165, 173–186, 274, 285–304, 306.
William Heckler: pages 22, 39, 45, 187, 198–199.
Ray Keane: pages 23–31, 242–254.
Trina Schart: pages 32–38, 39, 121, 142, 144, 281.
Paul Granger: pages 62–66, 68–72, 115–120, 272, 273.
Art Wood: pages 75–77, 79, 89, 157, 211, 214, 229.
Ed Young: pages 80–87, 90–95, 130, 131–140.
Witold Mars: pages 100–107, 109, 110–113.
Gordon Laite: pages 122–128.
Tom Sutton: pages 145–155.
Shannon Stirnweiss: pages 167–171.
John C. Wonsetler: pages 189–197.
Louis Cary: pages 200–209.
Don Sibley: pages 215–227.
Robert MacLean: pages 230–240, 241, 284.
Brian Wildsmith: pages 258–264, 267–270.
Nino Carbe: pages 275–279.

Acknowledgments

For permission to reprint copyrighted material, grateful acknowledgment is made to the following publishers, authors, and agents:

Abelard-Schuman Ltd., for "The Travelers and the Bear" and "The Date Gatherers." Reprinted from *Twenty-five Fables* by Norah Montgomerie by permission of Abelard-Schuman Ltd. All rights reserved. Copyright year 1961.

Abingdon Press, for "Why Cowboys Sing in Texas." From *Why Cowboys Sing, in Texas* by Le Grand. Copyright 1950 by Le Grand Henderson. By permission of Abingdon Press.

Isaac Asimov, for "How Does It Feel on the Moon?" written especially for this book.

Captain Edward L. Beach, USN, for "Following the Path of Magellan," written especially for this book.

Rowena Bennett, for "Witch Cat." Reprinted from *Story Parade* by permission of the author.

The Bobbs-Merrill Company, Inc., for "Ferdinand Magellan." From *A Book of Heroes* by Dorothy Heiderstadt, copyright © 1954 by The Bobbs-Merrill Company, Inc., used by special permission of the publishers.

Brandt & Brandt, for "Wilbur and Orville Wright" by Stephen Vincent Benét. From *A Book of Americans* by Rosemary and Stephen Vincent Benét. Holt, Rinehart and Winston, Inc. Copyright, 1933, by Rosemary and Stephen Vincent Benét. Copyright renewed, 1961, by Rosemary Carr Benét. Reprinted by permission of Brandt & Brandt.

Jonathan Cape Ltd., for "One Guess" from *The Complete Poems of Robert Frost*. Reprinted by permission of Jonathan Cape Ltd.

Carl Carmer, for "How Tony Beaver Built the Candy Dam," from *The Hurricane's Children*.

Child Life, for "Pegleg and the Whale" by Bill and Rosalie Brown, from *Child Life*, copyright 1948.

Marchette Chute, for "Dreams." Reprinted from *Child Life* by permission of the author.

Ruth H. Colby, for "Jack-O'-Lantern." From *Child Life*. Copyright 1935 by Rand McNally & Company.

Helen Reeder Cross, for "The Little Empress," retold by Helen Reeder Cross. Reprinted by special permission from *Jack and Jill* © 1953, The Curtis Publishing Co.

J. M. Dent & Sons, Ltd., for "The Tinder Box," translated by Mrs. Edgar Lucas from *Hans Andersen's Fairy Tales*.

The Devin-Adair Company, for "Moon-Cradle." From *Collected Poems* by Padraic Colum. Published by The Devin-Adair Company.

The Dial Press, Inc., for "The Flight of Icarus." Reprinted from *Stories of the Gods and Heroes* by Sally Benson. Copyright 1940 by Sally Benson and used with permission of the publishers, The Dial Press, Inc.

Dodd, Mead & Company, Inc., for "Four Limericks." Reprinted by permission of Dodd, Mead & Company, Inc. from *The Complete Nonsense Book* by Edward Lear and by permission of the Administrators of Constance S. Esther Rosa Cipelletti Lady Strachie, deceased.

Doubleday & Company, Inc., for "Could It Have Been a Shadow?" From *Goose Grass Rhymes* by Monica Shannon. Copyright 1930 by Doubleday & Company, Inc. Reprinted by permission of the publisher.

E. P. Dutton & Company, Inc., for "The Four Friends." From the book *When We Were Very Young* by A. A. Milne. Copyright, 1924, by E. P. Dutton & Company, Inc. Renewal, 1952, by A. A. Milne. Reprinted by permission of the publishers. For "The Tinder Box." Adapted from the book *Hans Andersen's Fairy Tales* by Hans Christian Andersen, translated by Mrs. Edgar Lucas. Children's Illustrated Classics. Adapted by permission of E. P. Dutton & Company, Inc.

Farrar, Straus & Cudahy, Inc., for "The Vanilla Village." Reprinted from *The Vanilla Village* by Priscilla Carden, by permission of Farrar, Straus & Cudahy, Inc. Copyright © 1952 by Priscilla Carden and Jay Hyde Barnum.

Harcourt, Brace & World, Inc., for "Ships." From *Magpie Lane* by Nancy Byrd Turner, copyright, 1927, by Harcourt, Brace & World, Inc.; renewed, 1955 by Nancy Byrd Turner and reprinted by permission of the publisher. For "Sprinter" from *Good Morning, America* by Carl Sandburg, copyright, 1928, © 1956, by Carl Sandburg. Reprinted by permission of Harcourt, Brace & World, Inc.

Harper & Row, Publishers, Inc., for Chapter 5, Chapter 11, and last paragraph of Chapter 10 from *Little House on the Prairie* by Laura Ingalls Wilder. Copyright 1935 by Laura Ingalls Wilder.

George G. Harrap & Company Ltd., for "Song of the Parrot" from *Alice-All-by-Herself* by Elizabeth Coatsworth. Reprinted by permission of George G. Harrap & Company Ltd.

Ethel L. Heins, for dramatization of "Doctor Know-All" from *Kinder- und Hausmärchen* by Wilhelm and Jacob Grimm, translated from the German by Paul Heins.

David Higham Associates Ltd., for "The King of China's Daughter" from *Collected Poems* by Edith Sitwell. Published by Macmillan & Company Ltd.

The Hokuseido Press Company Ltd., for four lines by Akinobô from *Haiku, Volume IV, Autumn-Winter* by R. H. Blyth.

Holt, Rinehart and Winston, Inc., for "One Guess." From *You Come Too* by Robert Frost. Copyright 1936 by Robert Frost. Reprinted by permission of Holt, Rinehart and Winston, Inc.

Houghton Mifflin Company, for "Texas Trains and Trails" and "A Song of Greatness." The selections from Mary Austin's *The Children Sing in the Far West*, copyright 1928, are reprinted by permission of and arrangement with Houghton Mifflin Company, the authorized publishers.

Osa Johnson, for adaptation of "First Adventures with the World" from *Tarnish* by Osa Johnson, copyright by Belle Leighty. Reprinted by permission of Belle Leighty.

Alfred A. Knopf, Inc., for two verses of "Measure Me, Sky!" Reprinted from *Slow Wall* together with *Nor Without Music* by Leonora Speyer. Copyright 1926, 1946 by Leonora Speyer. For "The Golden Tombo." Reprinted from *The Golden Tombo* by H. Tom Hall, by permission of Alfred A. Knopf, Inc. Copyright © 1959 by H. Tom Hall.

J. B. Lippincott Company, for "Sharp Ears, the Baby Whale." From *Sharp Ears*, by John Y. Beaty. Copyright 1938 by John Y. Beaty. Published by J. B. Lippincott Company. For "Pinocchio." From *Pinocchio* by Carlo Collodi. Published by J. B. Lippincott Company. For "A Dragon-Fly." From *Poems for Children* by Eleanor Farjeon. Copyright 1933 by Eleanor Farjeon. Published by J. B. Lippincott Company. For "Minnie" from *Poems for Children*. Copyright © 1938 by Eleanor Farjeon.

Shuh-yin Lu Mar, for "Weighing the Long-Nosed Giant." Retold by Shuh-yin Lu Mar.

The Macmillan Company, for "Prairie Fire." Adapted with permission of the publisher from *The Sod House* by Elizabeth Coatsworth. Copyright, 1954, by The Macmillan Company. For "Flint" from *Sing-Song* by Christina Rossetti. For "The Wilderness Is Tamed." Reprinted with permission of the publisher from *Away Goes Sally* by Elizabeth Coatsworth. Copyright, 1934, by The Macmillan Company. For "Night." Reprinted with permission of the publisher from *Stars To-night* by Sara Teasdale. Copyright, 1930, by Sara Teasdale Filsinger. Copyright, 1958, by Guaranty Trust Company of New York, Executor. For "Song of the Parrot." Reprinted by permission of the publisher from *Alice-All-by-Herself* by Elizabeth Coatsworth. Copyright, 1957, by The Macmillan Company.

Dorothy Hope McCroden, for "Onion Boy's Adventure." Reprinted by special permission from *Jack and Jill*, © 1953, The Curtis Publishing Company.

David McKay Company, Inc., for "The Woodcutter's Helper" from *Once the Hodja* by Alice Geer Kelsey. Copyright 1943, Alice Geer Kelsey, and Longmans, Green and Company, Inc.

Julian Messner, Inc., for adaptation of "Raffy and the Honkebeest" by Rita Kissin reprinted by permission of Julian Messner, Inc., copyright 1940 by Julian Messner, Inc.

Methuen & Company Ltd., for "The Four Friends" from *When We Were Very Young* by A. A. Milne.

William Morrow and Company, Inc., for "Henry and Beezus." From *Henry and Beezus* by Beverly Cleary, copyright 1952 by Beverly Cleary, by permission of William Morrow and Company, Inc.

Harold Ober Associates, Inc., for "Dragon-Fly" from *Poems for Children* by Eleanor Farjeon. Copyright 1933, 1951 by Eleanor Farjeon. Reprinted by permission of Harold Ober Associates, Incorporated. For "Minnie" from *Poems for Children* by Eleanor Farjeon. Copyright © 1938 by Eleanor Farjeon. Reprinted by permission of Harold Ober Associates, Incorporated.

Oxford University Press, for "Pippi Finds a Spink" from *Pippi in the South Seas* by Astrid Lindgren.

Laurence Pollinger Ltd., for "One Guess" from *The Complete Poems of Robert Frost*. Reprinted by permission of the publishers, Jonathan Cape Ltd., and the proprietors, Holt, Rinehart & Winston, Inc.

Rosalind Richards, for "Tom Tickleby and His Nose" by Laura E. Richards.

Marion Ruckel, for "If I Were a One-Legged Pirate" by Mildred Plew Meigs.

Russell & Volkening, Inc., for "Denis and the Cloud" by Elizabeth Enright. Copyright © 1940 by *Child Life*. Reprinted by permission of Russell & Volkening, Inc.

Scott, Foresman and Company, for "The Magic Carpet" by Gertrude Chandler Warner, from *1001 Nights*. Copyright 1954.

Simon and Schuster, Inc., for an adaptation of "Chanticleer and the Fox" ("The Nun's Priest's Tale") by Barbara Cooney, from *The Canterbury Tales* translated by Lumiansky. Copyright 1948 by Simon and Schuster, Inc. Reprinted by permission of the publisher.

The Society of Authors, for "Tillie" by Walter de la Mare. By permission of the Literary Trustees of Walter de la Mare and The Society of Authors as their representative. For "Momotara" by Rose Fyleman. By permission of The Society of Authors as the literary representative of the Estate of the late Miss Rose Fyleman.

The University Society, Inc., for an excerpt from "The Wishing Carpet." From *The Bookshelf for Boys and Girls,* copyright 1958, published by The University Society, Inc., New York, New York.

The Viking Press, Inc., for "In My Mother's House" from *In My Mother's House* by Ann Nolan Clark. Copyright 1941 by Ann Nolan Clark. Reprinted by permission of The Viking Press, Inc. For "Pippi Finds a Spink." From *Pippi in the South Seas* by Astrid Lindgren, copyright © 1959 by Astrid Lindgren. Reprinted by permission of The Viking Press, Inc.

Henry Z. Walck, Inc., for "Johnny and His Mule" and "Moon's A-Rising" from *Johnny and His Mule* by Ellis Credle. Copyright 1946 by Henry Z. Walck, Inc. Reprinted by permission.

Woodfield & Stanley, Ltd., for "The Wilderness Is Tamed" from *Away Goes Sally* by Elizabeth Coatsworth.

CONTENTS

Imagine That!

Animals All

Magic or Not

Brave and Bold

Live and Learn

Skyward Ho!

Little House on the Prairie

Why Cowboys Sing in Texas

By Le Grand

Everybody knows how cowboys sing today in Texas. But there was a time when cowboys did not sing in Texas. That was a lonely time, long ago. This story tells how song came to Texas cowboys. It is a story heard beside a campfire by the river called the Rio Grande, the story of why cowboys sing in Texas.

Slim Jim

Today cowboys sing in Texas. They sing, "Yippee yi" and they sing, "Yippee yay." Everybody knows how cowboys sing today in Texas. But it was not always so.

Things were quiet once in Texas. Long ago in the days when cowboys did not sing, things were quiet. Cowboys were silent then, and the most silent cowboy in all of Texas was Slim Jim Bean.

Once in that old and silent time, Slim Jim was guarding a herd of cattle at night. It was a long, dark night, and Slim Jim Bean was lonely. "I wish I could hear a little noise," he thought. "Any kind of a little noise that would not frighten the cows."

Slim Jim knew that if anything frightened the cows, they would stampede. They would stampede and run all over

13

Texas. It might take a month of Sundays to round them up again.

Slim Jim thought of just the noise he would like to hear. It was a song he sang when he was a boy. He remembered the words, and he remembered the tune.

"I believe I could sing that song again," he said. "Just a little song should not frighten the cows."

So Slim Jim opened his mouth and he sang. The song woke the cows. And they didn't like it. They couldn't stand that song.

A little black cow stampeded.

A big yellow cow stampeded.

Big ones and little ones, spotted ones and plain ones—they all stampeded. They stampeded all over Texas.

Slim Jim and the other cowboys rode out to round up all the cows.

They rode through the mesquite with its long straight thorns.

They rode through the Spanish dagger with its long sharp spikes.

They rode through the cat's-claw with its long curved briers.

And they rode through clumps of cactus with its long prickly needles.

But the thorns did not hurt

14

them, and the spikes did not hurt them, and the briers did not hurt them, and the needles did not hurt them because they wore leather cowboy chaps on their legs.

Slim Jim was the best rider and the best roper in all Texas. But it took him and the other cowboys half a month of Sundays to round up those cows.

"Now, listen!" the other cowboys said to Slim Jim. "No more singing in Texas."

And Slim Jim promised he would sing no more; he would sing no more in Texas.

That night Slim Jim went out to guard the cows again. It was very quiet, and Slim Jim was lonely. He thought about his song. The song kept running through his mind.

Slim Jim tried to keep his promise. He tried hard not to sing. But the song went round and round in his mind. It went round and round, round and round. Slim Jim couldn't hold it back. He opened his mouth and he sang his song.

And the cows didn't like it.

A little tan cow stampeded.

A big red cow stampeded.

Big ones and little ones, spotted ones and plain ones—they all stampeded. They stampeded all over Texas.

Slim Jim and the other cowboys had to ride through all those thorny bushes again. This time it took them nearly a whole month of Sundays to round up those cows.

"Now, listen!" the other cowboys said to Slim Jim. "There will be no more singing, no more singing in Texas."

"Boys," Slim Jim said, "I can't promise. It's lonely at night on this lone prairie. That song keeps running through my mind.

15

It goes round and round, round and round. And when that happens, I have to sing it."

Then Slim Jim got on his horse and he said, "I can't promise not to sing, so I will go away. I will go far away. I will find a place where there are no cows to be frightened by my singing." And Slim Jim rode away.

On the tenth day Slim Jim came to a river. It was a very dry river. It was so dry that it was dusty. So Slim Jim knew it was the Rio Grande. Everyone in Texas knows the Rio Grande is the dustiest river in the world.

There was a little water out in the middle, but not enough for the fish to swim in. They had to walk on the bottom. Slim Jim could see them walking around down there.

"Hm," he said. "A tasty fish would make a fine supper."

Slim Jim was a cowboy, not a fisherman. He had no fishhooks and he had no fishline. But Slim Jim saw something. He saw that there was only enough river to cover the smallest fish. The biggest ones were half out of water as they walked along the bottom.

Slim Jim was a cowboy, and he was a good roper. He was the best roper in all Texas. So he whirled his rope—and he roped a fish. Slim Jim camped on the riverbank, and he cooked his fish.

It was lonely there beside the river. Slim Jim's song kept running through his mind. He opened his mouth and he sang. He sang that song. And his song did not frighten the fish in

the Rio Grande. Not a single fish stampeded.

"This is the place for me," Slim Jim said. "I shall stay here beside the river, and sing, and be a fisherman."

So Slim Jim laid aside his leather cowboy chaps because a fisherman would not need them. And he stayed beside the river called the Rio Grande, and he fished, and he sang.

Yippee Yi, Yippee Yay

But while Slim Jim fished and sang there was trouble in Texas.

The other cowboys remembered Slim Jim's song. That song kept running through their minds. It went round and round, round and round. They just couldn't help it—they sang that song.

And the cows didn't like it. They couldn't stand that song.

A big brown cow stampeded.

A little white cow stampeded.

Big ones and little ones, spotted ones and plain ones—they all stampeded. They stampeded all over Texas.

The cowboys rode for a whole month of Sundays. But they couldn't get the cows rounded up again.

Then up spoke Cactus Pete of the Pecos country.

"Boys," he said, "we need help. Slim Jim Bean is the best cowboy in all Texas. We must get Slim Jim to help us round up those cows."

The other cowboys agreed. So they rode out to find Slim Jim. They rode all over Texas. They rode until they came to the river called the Rio Grande, and that was where they found Slim Jim, fishing.

"Cows are stampeding all over Texas, Slim Jim," they told him. "We must get them rounded up again or Texas will be plumb ruined. You must help us round up those cows, Slim Jim."

Slim Jim turned away from the river, and his voice rose loud and free.

"Slim Jim will ride and round 'em up!" he cried. "All you cowboys follow me."

So Slim Jim rode to round up the cows, the cows that were stampeding all over Texas. He rode through all those thorny bushes. And Slim Jim felt the thorns. He felt them because he was not wearing his chaps—the leather cowboy chaps he laid aside when he became a fisherman.

When he felt the mesquite thorns, Slim Jim shouted, "Yip!"

When he felt the Spanish dagger spikes, Slim Jim shouted, "Yippee!"

When he felt the cat's-claw briers, Slim Jim shouted, "Yi!"

When he felt the cactus needles, Slim Jim shouted, "Yay!"

And when he felt them all at the same time, Slim Jim shouted, "Yippee yi, yippee yay!"

Slim Jim rode through all the thorny bushes in Texas. And his voice rose loud and free, "Yip, yippee, yi, yay! Yippee yi, yippee yay!"

Everywhere that Slim Jim rode, the cows heard him—the cows that were stampeding all over Texas. They liked those new sounds that Slim Jim made. They stopped running to listen to Slim Jim's *yips* and *yippees* and *yis* and *yays*.

Then up spoke Cactus Pete of the Pecos country.

"Slim Jim," he said, "the cows like those yippee yi noises."

The other cowboys all said, "Make those noises again, Slim Jim. The yippee yi noises, the noises the cows like."

So Slim Jim did it. He made the noises again, and he made them again. He made a song out of those noises.

Yippee yi, yippee yay.

The other cowboys listened. They liked Slim Jim's new song. So they all joined in and sang.

Yippee yi, yippee yay.

The cows liked the new song. The big cows liked it, and the little cows liked it.

Big ones and little ones, spotted ones and plain ones—they all stopped to listen.

Then Slim Jim and the other cowboys rounded them up.

And that was the end of the big stampede in Texas.

And that is why cowboys sing today in Texas. They sing, "Yippee yi," and they sing, "Yippee yay." They sing, "Yippee yi, yippee yay." They sing Slim Jim's song today in Texas.

On Your Own

1. A tall tale is usually a story about someone who does astonishing things with the greatest of ease. What astonishing things did Slim Jim do?

2. Why did the other cowboys ask Slim Jim not to sing? Why did they change their minds? How did Slim Jim happen to invent his new song?

3. List on paper the names of the thorny bushes at the left below. Beside each one write the word at the right that describes it.

    (a) cat's-claw   needles

    (b) cactus   thorns

    (c) mesquite   spikes

    (d) Spanish dagger   briers

TEXAS TRAINS AND TRAILS

By Mary Austin

Whenever I ride on the Texas plains
I never hear the couplings cluck,
I never hear the trains
Go chuck-a-luck, chuck-a-luck, chuck-a-luck,
I never hear the engine snort and snuffle,
I never see the smoke plume, I never watch the rails,
But I see the moving dust where the beef herds shuffle,
And I think I am a cowboy,
A rope-and-tie-'em cowboy,
Punching Texas longhorns
On the Texas trails.
And the engine goes *Whoop!*
Whoopee, whoopala!
And the cars go *Ki-yi,*
Ki-yi, ki-yi, coma-la ki-yi,
  Whoopala,
Ki-yi!
  Whoop!

WITCH CAT

By ROWENA BENNETT

I want a little witch cat
 With eyes all yellow-green,
Who rides upon a broomstick
 Every Halloween,
Who purrs when she is taking off,
 Just like a purring plane,
And doesn't mind a tailspin
 Even in the rain.
I want a cat who dares to light
 The candle of the moon
And set its jack-o'-lantern face
 A-laughing like a loon.
I want a cat who laps the milk
 Along the Milky Way,
A cat of spunk and character
 As daring as the day;
But gentle-looking kittens
 Are in the stores to sell
And which cat is a witch cat,
 I really cannot tell.

Pippi Finds a Spink

By ASTRID LINDGREN

Pippi was a most unusual girl. She kept house by herself in a tumble-down place called Villa Villekulla. Her horse and monkey lived with her—but no grown-ups. Pippi could do almost any strange and impossible thing she thought of doing. She could throw people up in the air, chop down a tree, or lift her horse off the porch. She shared many of her adventures with Tommy and Annika, friends next door. With Pippi around, you never could tell what would happen next.

Pippi's Discovery

One morning Tommy and Annika came skipping into Pippi's kitchen as usual, shouting good morning. But there was no answer. Pippi was sitting in the middle of the kitchen table with Mr. Nilsson, the little monkey, in her arms and a happy smile on her face.

"Good morning," said Tommy and Annika again.

"Just think," said Pippi dreamily, "just think that I have discovered it—I and no one else!"

"What have you discovered?" Tommy and Annika wondered. They weren't in the least bit

23

surprised that Pippi had discovered something, because she was always doing that, but they did want to know what it was.

"What did you discover, anyway, Pippi?"

"A new word," said Pippi and looked at Tommy and Annika as if she had just this minute noticed them. "A brand-new word."

"What kind of word?" said Tommy.

"A wonderful word," said Pippi. "One of the best I've ever heard."

"Say it, then," said Annika.

"Spink," said Pippi triumphantly.

"Spink," repeated Tommy. "What does that mean?"

"If I only knew!" said Pippi. "The only thing I know is that it doesn't mean vacuum cleaner."

Tommy and Annika thought for a while. Finally Annika said, "But if you don't know what it means, then it can't be of any use."

"That's what bothers me," said Pippi.

"Who really decided in the beginning, anyway, what all the words should mean?" Tommy wondered.

"Probably a bunch of old professors," said Pippi. "People certainly are peculiar! Just think of the words they make up —'but' and 'stopper' and 'string' and words like that. Where they got them from, nobody knows. But a wonderful word like 'spink,' they don't bother to invent. How lucky that I hit on it! And you just bet I'll find out what it means, too."

She fell deep in thought.

"Spink! I wonder if it might be the top part of a blue flagpole," she said doubtfully.

"Flagpoles aren't blue," said Annika.

"You're right. Well then, I really don't know. . . . Or do you think it might be the sound you hear when you walk in the mud and it gets between your toes? Let's hear how it sounds! 'As Annika walked in the mud, you could hear the most wonderful spink, spink.'" She shook her head. "No, that's no good. 'You could hear the most wonderful *tjipp, tjipp*'—that's what it should be instead."

Pippi scratched her head. "This is getting more and more mysterious. But whatever it is, I'm going to find out. Maybe it can be bought in the stores. Come on, let's go and ask!"

Tommy and Annika had no objection. Pippi went off to hunt for her purse, which was full of gold coins. "Spink," she said. "It sounds as if it might be expensive. I'd better take a gold coin along." And she did. As usual Mr. Nilsson, the monkey, jumped up on her shoulder.

Then Pippi lifted the horse down from the veranda. "We're in a hurry," she said to Tommy and Annika. "We'll have to ride. Because otherwise there might not be any spink left when we get there. It wouldn't surprise me if the mayor had already bought the last of it."

When the horse came galloping through the streets of the little town with Pippi and

Tommy and Annika on his back, the children heard the clatter of his hoofs on the cobblestones and came happily running because they all liked Pippi so much.

"Pippi, where are you going?" they cried.

"I'm going to buy spink," said Pippi and brought the horse to a halt for a moment.

The children looked puzzled.

"Is it something good?" a little boy asked.

"You bet," said Pippi and licked her lips. "It's wonderful. At least it sounds as if it were."

The Search

In front of a candy shop Pippi jumped off the horse, lifted Tommy and Annika down, and in they went.

"I would like to buy a bag of spink," said Pippi. "But I want it nice and crunchy."

"Spink," said the pretty lady behind the counter, trying to think. "I don't believe we have that."

"You must have it," said Pippi. "All well-stocked shops carry it."

"Yes, but we've just run out of it," said the lady, who had never even heard of spink but didn't want to admit that her shop wasn't as well stocked as any other.

"Oh, but then you did have it yesterday!" cried Pippi eagerly. "Please, please tell me how it looked. I've never seen spink in all my life. Was it red-striped?"

Then the nice lady blushed prettily and said, "No, I really don't know what it is. In any case, we don't have it here."

Very disappointed, Pippi walked toward the door. "Then I have to keep on looking," she said. "I can't go back home without spink."

The next store was a hardware store. A salesman bowed politely to the children.

"I would like to buy a spink," said Pippi. "But I want it to be of the best kind, the one that is used for killing lions."

The salesman looked sly as a fox. "Let's see," he said and scratched himself behind the ear. "Let's see." He took out a small rake. "Is this all right?" he said as he handed it to Pippi.

Pippi looked indignantly at him. "That's what the professors would call a rake," said she. "But it happens to be a spink I wanted. Don't try to fool an innocent little child."

Then the salesman laughed and said, "Unfortunately we don't have the thing you wanted. Ask in the store around the corner which carries notions."

"Notions," Pippi muttered to Tommy and Annika when they came out on the street. "I just know they won't have it there." Suddenly she brightened. "Perhaps, after all, it's a sickness," she said. "Let's go and ask the doctor."

Annika knew where the doctor lived because she had gone there to be vaccinated.

Pippi rang the bell. A nurse opened the door.

"I would like to see the doctor," said Pippi. "It's a very serious case. A terribly dangerous disease."

"This way, please," said the nurse.

The doctor was sitting at his desk when the children came in. Pippi went straight to him, closed her eyes, and stuck her tongue out.

"What is the matter with you?" said the doctor.

Pippi opened her clear blue eyes and pulled in her tongue. "I'm afraid I've got spink," she said, "because I itch all over. And when I sleep my eyes close.

Sometimes I have the hiccups and on Sunday I didn't feel very well after having eaten a dish of shoe polish and milk. My appetite is quite hearty, but sometimes I get the food down my windpipe, and then nothing good comes of it. It must be the spink which bothers me. Tell me, is it contagious?"

The doctor looked at Pippi's rosy little face and said, "I think you're healthier than most. I'm sure you're not suffering from spink."

Pippi grabbed him eagerly by the arm. "But there is a disease by that name, isn't there?"

"No," said the doctor, "there isn't. But even if there were, I don't think it would have any effect on you."

Pippi looked sad. She made a deep curtsy to the doctor as she said good-by, and so did Annika. Tommy bowed. And then they went out to the horse, who was waiting at the doctor's fence.

Not far from the doctor's house was a high three-story

house with a window open on the upper floor. Pippi pointed toward the open window and said, "It wouldn't surprise me if the spink is in there. I'll dash up and see." Quickly she climbed up the waterspout. When she reached the level of the window, she threw herself heedlessly into the air and grabbed hold of the window sill. She hoisted herself up by the arms and stuck her head in.

In the room two ladies were sitting chatting. Imagine their astonishment when all of a sudden a red head popped over the window sill and a voice said, "Is there by any chance a spink here?"

The two ladies cried out in terror. "Good heavens, what are you saying, child? Has someone escaped?"

"That is exactly what I would like to know," said Pippi very politely.

"Maybe he's under the bed!" screamed one of the ladies. "Does he bite?"

"I think so," said Pippi. "He's supposed to have tremendous fangs."

The two ladies clung to each other. Pippi looked around curiously, but finally she said with a sigh, "No, there isn't as much as a spink's whisker around here. Excuse me for disturbing you. I just thought I would ask, since I happened to be passing by."

She slid down the waterspout and said sadly to Tommy and Annika, "There isn't any spink in this town. Let's ride back home."

And that's what they did. When they jumped down from the horse, outside the veranda, Tommy came close to stepping on a little beetle, which was crawling on the gravel path.

"Be careful not to step on the beetle!" Pippi cried.

All three bent down to look at it. It was such a tiny thing, with green wings that gleamed like metal.

"What a pretty little creature," said Annika. "I wonder what it is."

"It isn't a cockchafer," said Tommy.

"And no ladybug either," said Annika. "And no stag-beetle. I wish I knew what it was."

All at once a radiant smile lit up Pippi's face. "I know," she said. "It's a spink."

"Are you sure?" Tommy said doubtfully.

"Don't you think I know a spink when I see one?" said Pippi. "Have you ever seen anything so spinklike in your life?"

She carefully moved the beetle to a safer place, where no one could step on it. "My sweet little spink," she said tenderly. "I knew that I would find one at last. But isn't it funny! We've been hunting all over town for a spink, and here was one right outside Villa Villekulla all the time!"

On Your Own

1. What was Pippi's discovery? What were some of her guesses about the meaning of the word? Name the places that she went to try to find a spink. What did she decide a spink was?

2. How clever are you with words? The underlined words in these sentences are used in the story. See if you can figure out the meanings.
   (a) All well-stocked shops carry it.
   (b) Pippi brought the horse to a halt.
   (c) Ask in the store which carries notions.

3. Perhaps you can invent a new word. Use it in a sentence, or draw a picture to show what the word means.

Pinocchio

By CARLO COLLODI

Pinocchio was a wooden puppet. He was full of fun, but he often got into trouble, as he did when the puppet-master, Fire-eater, gave him four gold pieces to take home to his father. Instead, Pinocchio traveled with the Fox and the Cat. They told him that if he planted his gold pieces in the Field of Miracles, he could grow thousands of gold pieces. Later, dressed as two assassins, they tied him by his neck to a tree and tried to steal his gold pieces. The Fairy saved him, but Pinocchio was feeling quite ill—and no wonder.

Sick in Bed

As soon as the three doctors had left the room the Fairy approached Pinocchio, and having touched his forehead she realized that he was in a high fever that was not to be trifled with.

She therefore put a certain medicine in half a tumbler of water, and offering it to the puppet she said to him lovingly: "Drink it, and in a few days you will be cured."

Pinocchio looked at the tumbler, made a face, and then asked in a sad little voice:

"Is it sweet or bitter?"

"It is bitter, but it will do you good."

"If it is bitter water, I will not take it."

"Listen to me: drink it."

"I don't like anything bitter."

"Drink it, and when you have drunk it I will give you a lump of sugar to take away the taste."

"Where is the lump of sugar?"

"Here it is," said the Fairy, taking a piece from a gold sugar basin.

"Give me first the lump of sugar, and then I will drink that bad bitter water."

"Do you promise me?"

"Yes."

The Fairy gave him the sugar, and Pinocchio, having crunched it up and swallowed it in a second, said, licking his lips:

"It would be a fine thing if sugar was medicine! . . . I would take it every day."

"Now keep your promise and drink these few drops of water, which will restore you to health."

Pinocchio took the tumbler unwillingly in his hand and put the point of his nose to it; he then approached it to his lips; he then again put his nose to it, and at last said:

"It is too bitter! Too bitter! I cannot drink it."

"How can you tell that, when you have not even tasted it?"

"I can imagine it! I know it from the smell. I want first another lump of sugar . . . and then I will drink it! . . ."

The Fairy then, with all the patience of a good mamma, put another lump of sugar in his mouth, and then again presented the tumbler to him.

"I cannot drink it so!" said the puppet, making a thousand faces.

"Why?"

"Because that little pillow that is down there on my feet bothers me."

The Fairy removed the little pillow.

"It is useless. Even so I cannot drink it."

"What is the matter now?"

"The door of the room, which is half open, bothers me."

The Fairy went and closed the door.

"In short," cried Pinocchio, bursting into tears, "I will not drink that bitter water—no, no, no, no!"

"My boy, you will be sorry."

"I don't care."

"Your illness is serious."

"I don't care."

"The fever in a few hours will become worse and worse."

"I don't care."

"Are you not afraid?"

"I am not in the least afraid! . . . I would rather die than drink that bitter medicine."

At that moment the door of the room flew open, and four black rabbits entered carrying on their shoulders a little black box.

"What do you want with me?" cried Pinocchio, sitting up in bed in a great fright.

"We are come to take you," said the biggest rabbit.

"To take me? . . . But I do not want to go with you!"

"No? But you said you would rather die than take the bitter medicine that would cure you of the fever."

"Oh, Fairy, Fairy!" the puppet then began to scream, "give me the tumbler at once . . . be quick, in the name of pity, for I will not die—no . . . I will not die."

And taking the tumbler in both hands he emptied it in one swallow.

"We must have patience!" said the rabbits. "This time we have made our journey for nothing." And taking the little black box again on their shoulders they left the room, muttering between their teeth.

In fact, a few minutes afterwards Pinocchio jumped down from the bed quite well, because you must know that wooden puppets have the power of being rarely ill and of being cured very quickly.

The Fairy, seeing him running and rushing about the room as gay and as lively as a young cock, said to him:

"Then my medicine has really done you good?"

"Good? I should think so! It has restored me to life!"

"Then why on earth did you need so much pressing to make you take it?"

"Because you see that we boys are all like that! We are more afraid of medicine than of the illness."

"Disgraceful! Boys ought to know that a good medicine taken in time may save them from a serious illness, and perhaps even from death."

"Oh! but another time I shall not need so much pressing. I shall remember those black rabbits with the black box on their shoulders . . . and then I shall immediately take the tumbler in my hand, and down it will go!"

Telling a Lie

"Now come here to me," said the Fairy, "and tell me what happened to the gold pieces Fire-eater gave you."

"It came about," said Pinocchio, "that the two assassins

tried to steal my money. I had hidden it under my tongue, though, and I would not open my mouth."

"And the four gold pieces— where have you put them now?" asked the Fairy.

"I have lost them!" said Pinocchio; but he was telling a lie, for he had them in his pocket.

He had scarcely told the lie when his nose, which was already long, grew at once two fingers longer.

"And where did you lose them?"

"In the wood near here."

At this second lie his nose went on growing.

"If you have lost them in the wood near here," said the Fairy, "we will look for them, and we will find them, because everything that is lost in that wood is always found."

"Ah! now I remember all about it," replied the puppet, getting quite confused. "I didn't lose the four gold pieces; I swallowed them while I was drinking your medicine."

At this third lie his nose grew to such an extraordinary length that poor Pinocchio could not move in any direction. If he turned to one side he struck his nose against the bed or the windows, if he turned to the other he struck it against the walls or the door, if he raised his head a little he took the chance of sticking it into one of the Fairy's eyes.

And the Fairy looked at him and laughed.

"What are you laughing at?" asked the puppet, very much confused, and anxious at finding his nose growing so long.

"I am laughing at the lie you have told."

"And how can you possibly know that I have told a lie?"

"Lies, my dear boy, are found out immediately, because they are of two sorts. There are lies that have short legs, and lies that have long noses. Your lie, as it happens, is one of those that have a long nose."

Pinocchio, not knowing where to hide himself for shame, tried

to run out of the room; but he could not do so, for his nose had grown so much that it could no longer pass through the door.

The Fairy, as you can imagine, allowed the puppet to cry and to roar for a good half-hour over his nose. This she did to give him a severe lesson, and to correct him of the disgraceful fault of telling lies—the most disgraceful fault that a boy can have. But when she saw him quite disfigured, and his eyes puffed out of his head from weeping, she felt full of pity for him. She therefore beat her hands together, and at that signal a thousand large birds called Woodpeckers flew in at the window. They immediately perched on Pinocchio's nose, and began to peck at it so fast that in a few minutes his enormous and ridiculous nose was shortened to its usual size.

"What a good Fairy you are," said the puppet, drying his eyes, "and how much I love you!"

"I love you also," answered the Fairy; "and if you will remain with me, you shall be my little brother and I will be your good little sister."

On Your Own

1. What did the black rabbits do to make Pinocchio take his medicine?

2. What happened to Pinocchio after he told a lie? How do you think Pinocchio felt when the Fairy laughed at him? How do you think he felt after the Woodpeckers came?

3. Write on paper the word *Pinocchio*. Under it write the words that describe him. Then write *Fairy*. Under it write the words that describe her.

thoughtful	lively	patient	gay
naughty	good	cocky	kind

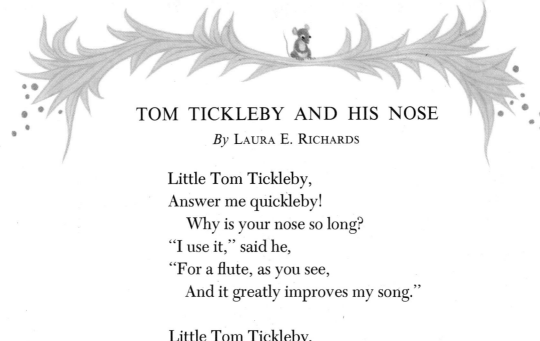

TOM TICKLEBY AND HIS NOSE

By Laura E. Richards

Little Tom Tickleby,
Answer me quickleby!
   Why is your nose so long?
"I use it," said he,
"For a flute, as you see,
   And it greatly improves my song."

Little Tom Tickleby,
Answer me quickleby!
   Why do you run so fast?
"I'm hoping," said he,
"If right swiftly I flee,
   To catch up with my nose at last!"

Tony Beaver and the Candy Dam

By CARL CARMER

Tony Beaver, a mighty lumberjack and a mighty man, built a candy dam to stop the flooding Eel River. Does this sound impossible? Not at all! You have only to use your imagination and follow Tony, who could do anything!

Tony Beaver

In the high West Virginia mountains, where the Eel River dashes down toward what mountain folks call the "Levels," is the lumber camp of Tony Beaver. It's pretty hard to find

40

because, in the first place, not even the best map of West Virginia shows the course of Eel River, and, in the second place, the camp is deep in the woods. But if you want to find it very much and if you set out into the mountains and use your imagination enough, you will get there.

Before long you will be in a big cook tent beside Eel River, and Tony Beaver will be saying, "How about a second piece of this apple pie made out of real West Virginia Golden Delicious apples?"

Tony Beaver had a yoke of oxen that could pull almost anything into the middle of next week. Each ox had a pair of horns with so much spread that it would take a blackbird six years to fly from the tip of one horn to the tip of the other. Tony never found anything his oxen couldn't pull to market except one of his especially grown West Virginia watermelons.

The watermelons in Tony's patch grew so big that even the smallest one wouldn't fit into the biggest wagon. So Tony wound a little melon with ropes and fastened the ropes to the ox harness. The oxen got the melon started all right; but when they got near Eel River, the traces broke and the melon rolled right down into the river and hit bottom so hard it burst.

Tony and his gang of lumberjacks jumped onto the seeds as they came to the surface and began yelling and singing and spinning the seeds with their feet. They put on the biggest drive ever seen on Eel River.

When they got down to the sawmill dam, they sold their drive as peeled logs. Some of the finest houses in West Virginia are made out of planks from those very watermelon seeds.

Building the Dam

Perhaps the best of all the stories about Tony Beaver is the one that tells how he built the candy dam. There had been an unusually wet fall in West Virginia one year, and Eel River had begun to rise above its banks. It got higher and higher, and pretty soon the little town near Tony's camp was in danger of being flooded and carried downstream.

Nobody seemed to know what to do until a little schoolboy said to his companions, "Let's go tell Tony Beaver about it. He can do anything."

So they started out to go to Tony's camp, but they got lost in the woods and would have wandered around for days if Tony Beaver had not heard they were coming and sent one of his loggers to find them.

He found them all right, and a little while after that they were in the big cook tent of Tony's camp, and Tony was saying,

"How about a second piece of that Golden Delicious apple pie?"

The children told Tony how high the river was getting and how they and their parents were in danger of being drowned. So Tony called to his men, and they all jumped on saw logs and rode them through the swift waters down the Eel River to the town, each lumberjack carrying one of the children back home. Then Tony took command.

"Open up your molasses storage houses," he told the men of the town, "and bring me every barrel of molasses you've got! And open up all your peanut storage houses and bring me every bag of West Virginia peanuts you can find!"

The men did what he told them, and Tony said to his crew of lumberjacks, "Roll those barrels up the river six miles to Blacksmith's Bend; then the rest of you folks drag along those bags of peanuts."

When everybody got to Blacksmith's Bend, Tony said to his men, "Knock in the heads of those barrels and pour the molasses into the river. Now, the rest of you folks start shelling peanuts and throw the peanuts into the water."

So everybody was as busy as a bee for a long time, and finally all the molasses and all the peanuts were in the river.

"I nearly forgot something!" shouted Tony Beaver.

He dashed back to his camp and came running back waving a vinegar bottle as big as a candy factory and a salt shaker as big as the Capitol Building in Washington. He emptied the vinegar and the salt into the stream.

"Let's follow this downstream," said Tony Beaver, "and see what happens."

The sun came out about then, and the whole crowd, walking downstream, saw the river begin to thicken up. As the sun got hotter and hotter, the river got thicker and thicker and slower and slower. Just before they got to town, the flow stopped altogether; and the river began to pile up a shiny, brownish dam full of big white lumps. The dam got bigger and bigger until it protected the town completely. There was no more danger of flood now.

"Break off a piece of the dam and taste it," said Tony to the schoolboy who had thought of telling him of the danger. So the schoolboy bit off a piece and tasted it.

"It's peanut brittle!" he cried. So it was! And all the children of the town had all the peanut brittle they wanted all winter as a result of Tony Beaver's building the candy dam.

On Your Own

1. Tall tales have many ideas that stretch the truth. Below is one from the story. See how many others you can find.

   Each ox had a pair of horns with so much spread that it would take a blackbird six years to fly from the tip of one horn to the tip of the other.

2. Tony Beaver did these three things to build the candy dam:
   (a) He poured molasses into the river.
   (b) He threw peanuts into the water.
   (c) He emptied vinegar and salt into the stream.
   Tell the whole story in pictures or words.

FOUR LIMERICKS

By Edward Lear

There was a Young Lady of Norway,
Who casually sat in a doorway;
When the door squeezed her flat, she exclaimed, "What of that?"
This courageous Young Lady of Norway.

There was an Old Person whose habits
Induced him to feed upon Rabbits;
When he'd eaten eighteen, he turned perfectly green,
Upon which he relinquished those habits.

There was a Young Lady of Bute,
Who played on a silver-gilt flute;
She played several jigs, to her Uncle's white Pigs,
That amusing Young Lady of Bute.

There was a Young Lady whose nose
Was so long that it reached to her toes;
So she hired an Old Lady, whose conduct was steady,
To carry that wonderful nose.

45

Thinking It Through

1. In what story did each of the following things happen? Write each title. Who did each thing? Write the name beside the title that goes with it.
   - (a) He built a candy dam.
   - (b) He made up a cowboy song.
   - (c) He told a lie.
   - (d) She discovered a new word.

2. In making candy, what two things did Tony Beaver almost forget to put in? Find directions for peanut brittle in a cookbook. Compare these directions with Tony Beaver's. You might like to try out one set of directions.

3. Perhaps you would like to tell or write a tall tale of your own. Use your imagination to invent a new tall tale character, or make up another story about Slim Jim or Tony.

4. This story of Pinocchio or another from the book *Pinocchio* would make a fine puppet show. Write out your plans.
   - (a) How many scenes will you have?
   - (b) Which characters will you use?
   - (c) Who will play each part?

5. Make a picture dictionary of words that you invent.

6. Find other stories of Pippi in the books *Pippi Longstocking, Pippi Goes on Board,* and *Pippi in the South Seas.*

Raffy and the Honkebeest

By RITA KISSIN

Raffy, the baby giraffe, wanted to be the Champion Runner of the veldt. But how could he beat the Honkebeest?

Raffy

Raffy was born in Africa in a thicket of bush and thorn. All day long the sun shone down on the wide plains of hard, dry earth called the veldt. But Raffy did not mind the dust and the heat. For he was a baby giraffe, and the veldt is home to baby giraffes. Besides, his mother was there to lick his face and blow the dust from his brown spotted coat and make him comfortable.

At first Raffy could scarcely walk at all. His legs were wobbly, and when he stood up, he had to lean against his mother to keep from falling. But he drank a great deal of milk, and little by little his legs grew stronger. Soon he was walking very well indeed.

Then his mother took Raffy to the water hole, where he met ever so many animals who lived on the veldt too. He met the hartebeest with horns straight over his eyes.

And the little gazelles who had soft tufts at the end of their tails.

The wildebeests were there, too, with their funny white beards, and the warthog, and the black-and-white-striped zebras, and the greedy waterbucks, and the tiny dik-diks with their bright brown eyes.

48

Close beside his mother, Raffy stood and watched them. Most interesting of all, he thought, was Longhorn, the fastest antelope, who jumped all the way across the water hole. How splendid to jump like that! Raffy wished he could do it.

"Never mind," his mother said to him. "If you keep growing nicely, you will be much taller than he is. Perhaps you will be taller than I am. And I am so tall that every one of these animals must look up to me."

Raffy turned his head. Yes, his mother was the tallest animal of all. He felt very proud of her.

The next day, she began teaching Raffy his lessons. She showed him how to spread his legs apart so that he could bend down and drink without falling over. She showed him how to pull down tree branches so that he could eat the tenderest leaves. And over and over again, she told him to stay away from the jungle, where fierce animals were hiding among the

trees. Raffy's father went into the jungle one day, just before Raffy was born, and he never came back. Raffy's mother didn't want that to happen to her baby.

So at night she made Raffy listen carefully to the roar of the lion in the forest and the cough of the leopard and the laugh of the hyena.

"These animals are not your friends," she told him. "Always, always stay away from the jungle where they live."

But of all the lessons his mother taught him, Raffy liked his running best. At first, when she started galloping across the veldt, Raffy was left far behind. But he kept on trying to catch up with her, and every day he ran just a little bit better than the day before. Sometimes, while his mother rested at noon near the water hole, Raffy would steal away and practice by himself.

Raffy sang softly to himself then:

"Loppity, leppity, lippity, lo!
I'll be Champion Runner
Of the veldt, I know."

One day, to his mother's great surprise, he caught up with her. In a few weeks, he was running as fast as she was. Then he began to race the other animals, the swift-footed antelopes and the gazelles. Sometimes he lost. Sometimes he won. But no matter how he came out, he was always ready to try again.

"I can beat even you now," he cried to Longhorn at the water hole one day.

Longhorn looked at Raffy, pointed his ears, cocked his head, and began to run. Raffy rushed after him. On and on raced Longhorn, never glancing back. He jumped ditches and he sailed over bushes like a bird. Try as he might, Raffy could not catch up with him. For Raffy couldn't jump across ditches or sail over bushes. He had to run around them, and that took time.

"Oh, dear," thought Raffy. "I do wish I could beat him."

At that his wish came true, for Longhorn, not being as young as Raffy, had become very tired, so tired, in fact, that he slowed down and leaned against a tree, puffing hard. And Raffy, who was not tired at all, caught up with him, passed him, then turned around with a *very* pleased expression on his face.

"All right, you've beaten me," gasped Longhorn. "But I know one animal you *can't* beat—the speeding Honkebeest."

A Honkebeest! What was that? Raffy knew he had never seen one at the water hole, nor had he heard his mother mention one.

"Does Honkebeest run fast?" he now asked.

Longhorn nodded. "Faster than your mother, faster than a gazelle, faster, even, than I, the fastest antelope," he said.

"What does he look like?" asked Raffy.

"Look like!" snorted Longhorn. "He is a monster."

Then and there, Raffy made up his mind to find a Honkebeest and race him. But where was a Honkebeest to be found? Back at the water hole, Raffy counted over all the animals. There were the hartebeest and the gazelle and the warthog and the wildebeest and the waterbucks and the dik-diks—all of them. But there was not one that was new or strange, not one that looked like a monster.

When Raffy asked his mother about the Honkebeest, she said, "Of course I have seen him. Every up-to-date veldt animal knows the Honkebeest. Keep your eyes open and you'll recognize him. Besides, he goes *honk-honk*."

So Raffy kept his eyes open for the Honkebeest. When he and his mother ran across the veldt, he looked in every direction. But day after day, no strange new animal came racing.

Neck and Neck

One afternoon, when Raffy wasn't thinking about anything special, he looked up to see a very strange creature crossing the veldt. It had a long dark body, humped as if ready to spring. Its head had a blunt snout, and two large fiery eyes looked out above wide teeth. Its tail was made of fog. But even more strange were its flat, round legs that whirled around and around, faster than the wind, it seemed.

"I don't know what you are, but I'm going to beat you!" declared Raffy, running pell-mell after the strange creature.

"Honk-honk!" snorted the beast at him.

And Raffy knew. This was the Honkebeest, the Honkebeest that Longhorn said Raffy must beat if he wished to be the Champion.

Raffy ran faster than ever.

"Honk-honk!" snorted the creature again, leaping along and making his tail into a black cloud. *"Honk-honk!"*

"You needn't keep *honk-honking* at me!" cried Raffy. "I'm not scared of you. And what's more, I'm going to beat you."

Off they went in a cloud of dust. On and on they sped, with Honkebeest still ahead, but with Raffy getting closer to him every minute. On and on, until they came to the water hole, where Raffy's mother was waiting for him.

"Look!" she cried to the other veldt animals. "Just look at

that! Raffy is racing the Honkebeest!"

The hartebeests and the gazelles and the wildebeests and the waterbucks and the dik-diks all looked.

"I wish you well!" cried Tommy Gazelle.

"I wish you luck!" cried Waterbuck.

"You must be quick!" cried little Dik-dik.

Then all together they shouted, "Go to it, Raffy! Beat him! Beat the Honkebeest!"

But the warthog didn't join in. Stopping his drinking only long enough to see what the excitement was about, he inched out still farther into the water hole, wheezing, "What a ridiculous sight! Raffy racing the Honkebeest with the whirling legs. A baby giraffe thinking he can win the championship of the veldt. It certainly makes me laugh."

Raffy was much too far away by that time to hear what the warthog was saying. But even if he had heard it, he would not have stopped. For he was certain that he was much closer to the Honkebeest than he had been before they passed the water hole. And Raffy was sure that in just a few moments he would pass him.

Now with another *"Honk!"* the Honkebeest went faster than ever. Raffy went faster, too. But his mouth felt dry, and his tongue was thick with dust. How good it would seem to be at the water hole with his mother, putting his nose down into the clear, cool water!

But Raffy didn't turn around to go back to the water hole.

He kept right on. "I must catch him and pass him. Catch him and pass him. Catch him and pass him," he said over and over to himself as he ran.

Very shortly it began to look as though Raffy really would catch up. Closer and closer he came to the snorting beast. Then, "Here I am, watch out!" cried Raffy. "I'm going to beat you any minute!"

And with that he took a bite at the tail of fog.

"Here I go!" shouted Raffy. "Here I go around you."

He spoke too soon. Just then, a flying stone cut his foot, and Raffy slowed down. But he didn't stop. "I'll run until I drop," he declared. "I'm not going to give up."

Now so much dust got into his eyes that he could scarcely see. Still he kept on. And once more closer and closer he came to the Honkebeest. Closer and closer until he ran past the Hon-kebeest's tail, past his stomach, and up beside his head. Neck and neck they raced! The sun burned down upon them. The

air felt like fire. And soon Raffy was breathing so hard it seemed to him that his chest would puff up and burst. There was a pain in his chest, too.

"But if this Honkebeest can stand it, I can," he gasped. "All I need to do now is go just a little faster, and I'll be the Champion, the Champion Runner of the veldt."

So Raffy did go a little faster. But the Honkebeest immediately went a little faster, too. On they sped, across the dry veldt toward the mountains.

"This is the time!" thought Raffy now. "I'll put on a little more speed, and then I'll have him!"

Just then the Honkebeest turned suddenly toward a forest which Raffy hadn't noticed before. Straight toward the trees it went. Raffy caught his breath and slowed down. From every one of those trees hung moss and vines, just the place for the wild animals who were his enemies to hide. It was the dangerous jungle. Should he follow the Honkebeest into it, even though his mother had told him never, never to go in among the trees?

"Perhaps it would be all right if I went just a little way," Raffy decided. "I don't hear any lion roaring or a leopard coughing or a hyena laughing."

He started forward, then stopped suddenly. Where was the Honkebeest? Raffy looked in all directions. There wasn't a sign of the Honkebeest on the veldt or among the trees of the jungle. Only the moss and the vines waved in the wind.

"Oh, dear, oh, dear!" sighed Raffy sadly. "I'm sure I could have beaten him in another five minutes."

Champion Runner of the Veldt

Just then Raffy heard a sound from among the trees. Raffy jumped, ready to run away. Perhaps a lion was watching him!

It wasn't a lion. It was a friendly little monkey, coming out from behind a tree trunk and grinning at him. "I saw you from the top of the tallest tree in my jungle," she told Raffy. "It was a good race, mighty good. And if you will do as I say, you can beat the Honkebeest yet."

"How can I beat him when he's gone?" Raffy asked the friendly little monkey.

"He isn't gone. He's just out of sight," answered the monkey. "Every day he does the same thing. He comes along here, and then he runs through the jungle on the road. Then he

turns around and comes back another way on the veldt. Would you like to have me show you a short cut through the jungle to the place where he comes out on the veldt? Then you can race him again."

The monkey's voice was so kind that Raffy was no longer afraid. "I should like it very much, thank you," he replied. "But my mother told me never to go into the jungle. The lion and the leopard and the hyena live there, and we giraffes don't like them."

The monkey considered. Then she said, "Did your mother tell you not to go *around* the jungle?"

Raffy couldn't remember that she did.

"Very well, then," said the monkey, "I'm sure you wouldn't be afraid if you walked around the jungle with me and my family. Come with me to my family tree and we'll get the children. It is just at the edge of the jungle. When you hear the noise they make, you will realize

that you are safe near the dangerous jungle!"

So Raffy followed the monkey to the family tree. High in its branches was a bed made of leaves and twigs, and over the ledge of the bed three small monkeys' heads looked down.

"Come, children!" called Raffy's friend. "We're going to have fun!"

Down from the tall tree swung the little monkeys and onto Raffy's back. "It's a slide!" they shouted.

All three of them slid down Raffy's smooth back, then walked about on their hands to show Raffy how pleased they were to meet him.

"If you obey nicely, children, you may go with us," their mother told them. "This gentleman wishes to race the Honkebeest, and I have promised to take him around the jungle to the place where he can find him."

"We'll obey," promised the little monkeys. "But please let us ride on the gentleman's back!"

"I don't mind," said Raffy good-naturedly. "But you must get off when the Honkebeest comes along. I never could beat him with three monkeys on my back!"

"We'll get off when the Honkebeest comes along," promised the three little monkeys, swinging up into the family tree, then dropping down on his back. One of them rode on his tail. And off they all started together to find the Honkebeest.

High above them in the trees near the edge of the jungle, monkeys were calling to each other. And here and there and everywhere, brightly colored birds flew about. It was a beautiful sight, but Raffy couldn't help being worried.

"Don't be afraid," said the mother monkey. "Those are my friends up in the trees. They will let us know if a lion or a leopard or a hyena comes along."

A hanging vine hit Raffy in the face just then, and he jumped. The three little monkeys squealed loudly.

"Besides, we are almost there," the mother monkey went on.

At that, *"Honk-honk, honk-honk,"* sounded from the jungle.

It was the Honkebeest. "Quick, this way!" cried the mother monkey. "Children, slide down at once."

In great excitement, the three little monkeys slid off Raffy's tail. And Raffy followed the mother monkey to an opening in the trees at the edge of the jungle. Sure enough, there was the Honkebeest speeding across the veldt.

"Thank you!" Raffy cried hurriedly, and, like a flash, Raffy ran after the rushing monster. He forgot about the flying stones. He paid no attention to the dust and the heat. His breath came fast, and his heart beat like thunder. But he knew that this time he would win. Raffy sang softly to himself.

"Loppity, leppity, lippity, lo!
I'll be Champion Runner
Of the veldt, I know!"

Once more Raffy caught up with the Honkebeest. Once more he took a bite of his tail. Once more he went past his stomach and his nose. Once more they ran neck and neck. But whenever Raffy tried to get ahead, the Honkebeest put on more speed. It was all most discouraging.

Raffy was just beginning to think perhaps it would be better to wait until another day to finish the race, when suddenly the Honkebeest started to puff as though he were trying to catch his breath. Then he made queer noises in his throat and hissed through his teeth. His whole body shivered and shook frightfully.

"He is trying to frighten me," thought Raffy, "and make me stop. Well, I won't. I'll show him." And taking a deep breath, he ran on.

For a little way the Honkebeest raced beside Raffy. Then with a deep grunt, he stopped altogether. Like a flash, Raffy sailed on ahead and on to the water hole.

Everyone was there—Longhorn and the gazelles and the wildebeests and the hartebeests and the zebras and the water- bucks, the little dik-diks and all the rest. In the center of them all stood Mother Giraffe, her head held proudly high.

"Hurrah! Hurrah!" they all shouted when Raffy came up.

"I wished you well!" cried Tommy Gazelle.

"I brought you luck!" cried Waterbuck.

"Oh, you were quick!" cried little Dik-dik.

Even lazy Warthog joined in. "My young friend," he said, "I apologize for the remarks which you do not know I made. I am delighted you beat the Honkebeest, and I congratulate you upon being Champion Runner of the veldt."

"We're all glad," cried the other animals. "We all con- gratulate you."

"We congratulate you, too," shouted the three little monkeys and their mother, breathlessly joining the happy party.

Then each little monkey and each one of the other animals made a deep bow to Raffy, Champion Runner of them all.

On Your Own

1. What was the Honkebeest? Why were you surprised to find out it was not an animal?
2. What did Raffy keep saying to himself to keep up his courage? Do you sometimes say something to keep up your courage? If so, what?
3. What lessons did Raffy's mother teach him? Which one did Raffy like best? What lessons could you learn from Raffy?
4. List on paper the names of the animals that wanted Raffy to win. Which animal helped him most? Put a star by her name.

SONG OF THE PARROT

By ELIZABETH COATSWORTH

Far off, far off
Those forests lie
Beneath a heavy
Molten sky

Where I was born.
Oh, never more
At dusk shall I hear
Lions roar,

Nor see the monkeys
Leap and sway
From branch to branch
At dawn of day!

Behold me now,
Across the sea,
Watching mild ladies
Pour out tea!

First Adventures with the World

By OSA JOHNSON

Osa Johnson lived for a long time in Africa, where she came to know much about lions. This is her story of the lion cub, Tarnish. Tarnish learned that the world is enormous and wonderful—but dangerous.

Tarnish

The old lioness was sunning herself in the early morning. Sparkles of dew clung to the grasses, shining like diamonds as the sun rose. The distant blue hills cast long shadows on the plains. The cold of the night had passed.

The lioness's cubs, Tarnish and Fat and Thin, rolled and crawled all over her. Their little bowed front legs and their great big feet just managed to get them around. Their almond eyes gave a sleepy-kitten look to their little moon faces.

Tarnish spent some time trying to catch the long black tuft of hair on the end of his mother's tail. Back and forth, back and forth, she switched it, just out of reach of Tarnish's batting paws.

Soon all three of her cubs were pouncing after it. What a wonderful game, to catch that switching tail! The cubs crept up on it and leaped after it, until the sun was well above the hills. Then they pounced on their mother for their breakfasts.

The cubs were full and sleepy. And as the sun grew warmer and shone on their golden furry hides, they curled up to sleep— all except Tarnish. He rolled over on his back with his four big feet in the air to get the sun on his stomach. That was where it felt best to him.

As he lay there on his back, he could sniff the sweet-smelling morning wind. The wind carried the spicy smells of grass and weeds and wild bushes from the great wide fields warming under the sun. From above him came the fragrance of blossoms.

Tarnish dozed. The world was enormous and wonderful. But a young cub has to sleep a lot if he is to grow strong enough to see the world in all its enormousness and all its wonder.

He woke suddenly at a tap from his mother's paw. He was warm, and the sun was high in the sky. It was time to be off, to seek cover from the heat of the day.

The old lioness mother went stalking on ahead over the rocks and down the long, winding *donga*, the steep-sided ditch, that led from their cave. The three cubs did their best to keep up with her.

At first they went at a little trot on their fat, padded paws. But their mother was getting too far ahead. Tarnish knew he must stay closer to that big, warm animal, his mother—no telling what might come pouncing at him from behind a bush or up at him from out of the long grasses. No doubt about it, his mother was getting too far ahead.

Suddenly, to his surprise, Tarnish left the ground in a bound. And he kept on bounding. As his feet hit the ground, they bounced him up again.

This was wonderful. It made him go much faster. His legs sprang out with him. The grass and bushes tickled his stomach as he leaped through them. He was running.

His mother never stopped or waited, but her walk slowed down. The old lioness did not look behind, but she knew where her cubs were.

Zoom! There was a great drumming sound almost under Tarnish's whiskers. A partridge flew up with a flutter of feathers, making its partridge call.

Tarnish stopped short. Was this the end of the world? His tail went up, and his ears went up. But after that first great rush of feathers beating the air, all was quiet again.

Quiet lay on the grasses, with only the small swish of beetles

and bugs to shiver the silence of the fields. Tarnish stood dead still, listening. Suddenly he bounded after his mother. He caught up with her long before Fat and Thin came along.

When they were all together, the old lioness led them to the shade of a thorn tree for a little rest. They had had the first bound, the first leap, the first partridge, and the first run. That was enough for the moment. She lay down with her cubs in the long grass to rest.

Tarnish rested his little body, but his eyes were busy. Deep

64

in the grasses, he saw another jungle, a jungle of bugs and creeping things. And there was a long, golden-brown twisting stick that slid silently on its way —the snake. Tarnish put his nose on his paws and watched.

Deep in the grasses, he saw a crawling world of colored beetles. Dark red and royal blue beetles moved around the grass roots. Golden beetles and spotted beetles went hurrying about their buggy business. He saw the big black rhinoceros beetle, with two tiny horns on its nose.

And scorpions! Tarnish saw them—golden scorpions and black scorpions—like long-tailed spiders crawling on the bottom of a sea of grass. He saw the sharp-horned stings on their tails. And he lay very still. For even a lion's paw could be stung by a scorpion. Tarnish kept his paws tucked under him. He took no chances. The day before he had been stung by a bee. A bee was a bug, and he knew what a bug was!

Danger!

After a while the lion family got up and went on their way.

They had not gone far, however, when out from a dark round hole in the ground crawled a queer, fat animal. Coming from it was a delicious pig smell that made the water trickle from the cubs' jaws.

But this animal was not like other animals. Instead of backing into its hole at the sight of a big lioness and three lion cubs not more than three shadows away, this strange animal came rattling right toward them.

The old lioness whipped her tail as a danger signal and gave a soft, low warning growl that meant: Get back in the bushes, you little cubs, away from this strange creature coming at us from its hole.

But the cubs were too adventuresome that day, and they missed the danger signal of their mother's tail. They did not pay attention to her warning growl.

The queer, fat animal kept coming toward them. As it

looked at them with its two black shiny eyes, the animal suddenly rattled all over and became twice as big, with its hair spiked out in all directions.

This animal was a porcupine; it had hair like other animals, but mixed with its thick hairs were many sharp quills. It was just too bad for any creature that came too close. The porcupine's quills would stick like arrows in the flesh of any animal that touched him.

Did Tarnish and the other two cubs know this? They did not. Tarnish rose to his toes, raised his tail, and bounced sideways at the animal. Fat and Thin bounced at the same time.

Their mother watched. She had given the danger signal.

The cubs had missed it. Now they would have to learn for themselves about porcupines, the quick way, once and forever.

Tarnish faced the porcupine.

The porky went for Tarnish, and Tarnish batted him with his paw.

Poor Tarnish! He gave a cry of pain as he pulled back his paw, stuck full of long black-and-white quills.

Thin grabbed at the animal and turned back howling, three sharp quills stuck in her nose.

Fat just backed up as fast as she could and watched her brother and sister as they tore out the sharp quills and howled with pain.

The old lioness watched them, but she did not help. They had

to learn for themselves. Once she had learned for herself.

But then, she had learned something else. For, like wild pig and warthog, porcupine flesh is very tasty and delicious for lions to eat. And the lioness was wise and knew all about quills. She knew there were no quills on the porky's head.

Old fat porky—feeling safe, as he usually was in his quills— almost walked right into the lion's jaws. When he realized his danger, it was too late.

While Tarnish and Thin lay there, growling and pulling and batting out the quills, their mother had a delicious fat porcupine to eat, all by herself.

Not until later did she go over to lick and comfort her whimpering cubs. After all, they were just little babies. With her teeth, she carefully helped them pull the quills out of their paws and noses. She licked their first wounds.

Then she picked up Tarnish by the back of the neck and carried him, because his paw hurt. And the other two little cubs followed her home to the cave for a long, warm sleep.

On Your Own

1. What did Tarnish see, hear, smell, and feel? Make a list. Here is a beginning.

See	Hear
royal blue beetles	swish of beetles

Smell	Feel
wild bushes	warm sun

2. How did the lioness warn her cubs of danger? Do you think she was gentle and kind with her cubs? Give your reasons.

3. Why did the lioness let the cubs fight alone? How do you think they felt? Why do you think so?

Sharp Ears, the Baby Whale

By JOHN Y. BEATY

Sharp Ears, a baby whale, was born near an island in the West Indies. When he was a few months old, he and his mother swam to the warm waters of the Gulf Stream near the Gulf of Mexico. There they joined a gam, or herd, of whales. Soon twenty baby whales, each with his mother, began a long and dangerous journey.

The Travelers

In the warm Gulf Stream, Sharp Ears and the other baby whales swam and played together. Their mothers began to give them more and more food. Though the babies themselves did not know it, they were getting ready for a very long journey.

Each day the mothers went to the bottom of the sea, catching dozens of giant squid to eat.

Then they gave their babies more milk than ever before. Both babies and mothers grew a great deal more blubber than usual. This blubber, which is the whale's overcoat, is very much needed on the whale's long journeys. It keeps them warm and their bodies burn it up for food. Sharp Ears' blubber and that of his young playmates soon grew to be four inches thick. That of their mothers was nearly eight inches thick.

Sharp Ears' gam was still in the Atlantic Ocean off the eastern coast of South America, but the whales wished to go to the Pacific Ocean. The only way a whale can get from the Atlantic Ocean to the Pacific Ocean is to swim around Cape Horn at the southern end of South America, or around the Cape of Good Hope at the southern end of Africa. Sharp Ears' gam was headed toward Cape Horn.

One day, as soon as the sun was up, Sharp Ears' mother signaled him to start. He had no idea that they had thousands of miles to travel, but he did know what his mother meant him to do, so he swam to her at once. Soon all forty whales were traveling south together. There was no playing among the calves now. The mothers kept their noses pointed south, and the calves had to keep up with them.

They had left the Gulf Stream, but the water was still

warm, for they were near the Equator. Very comfortable in the warm water, the whales traveled more slowly than before, but they kept steadily on their course every day. From the minute the sun rose in the morning, until an hour or two after sunset, they continued their way. After several days of steady travel, the calves became used to it, and the gam was able to go farther in a day. The whales did not need to stop to rest so long or so often.

The mother whales went to the bottom for food only once a day now. Even the babies' food became less and less. But Sharp Ears was a very good traveler. When his mother did not give him nearly as much milk as before, he did not care. Swimming along safely under her big body, he was happy with things as they were.

As they traveled farther and farther south, the water became colder. Then they saw icebergs. The icebergs delighted Sharp Ears. Whenever his mother would allow him, he would swim around one. Then if it were not too large, he would dive to find the bottom of it. Sometimes the bottom of an iceberg was so far under the water that the little calf did not have time to explore it. The icebergs were moving. Sharp Ears liked to put his big nose against one to see if he could make it move faster. Often, when Sharp Ears went far below in his exploring, he could feel a strong current. It was this current which was moving the iceberg.

A Terrifying Adventure

At last the gam reached Cape Horn at the southern end of South America. And it was while the whales were near Cape Horn that Sharp Ears had one of the most terrifying adventures of his life. He had been exploring an iceberg, one side of which had a flat platform, only a little above the surface of the water.

With his right eye Sharp Ears looked at the iceberg. Then he dived into the water for further exploring. He rose to the surface on the side of the iceberg away from his mother.

Sharp Ears was swimming along when he came face to face with a strange whale which was much smaller than himself. Even though the stranger had a cruel-looking mouth, with teeth on both upper and lower jaws, Sharp Ears was not afraid. He swam right on, minding his own business. But just as he was passing the other

whale, it suddenly opened its jaws and attacked him. It was a killer whale.

Sharp Ears was so surprised that he scarcely knew what to do. The sharp teeth cut through his fin, tearing large holes in his blanket of blubber. Sharp Ears sounded, but instead of going all the way down, he turned and swam to the surface again. The killer whale kept close beside him. Trying his best to escape, Sharp Ears leaped above the surface of the water an unusually long distance. He landed on the low part of the iceberg.

At this moment Sharp Ears' mother appeared. Before the killer whale could get away, she had him in her mouth, her big jaw with its sharp teeth snapping shut on the stranger's body.

But her baby was now trapped on the iceberg! And it was no easier for him to move there on the ice than on land. His body was far too heavy for his fins to be of help to him. Helplessly he signaled to his mother.

From one side of the iceberg to the other she swam, looking at Sharp Ears first from one eye, then from the other. She poked her big nose out of the water. She turned her body around, looking in all directions. There Sharp Ears lay on the iceberg, not knowing how to get back into the water. His head was near one edge. The ice beneath him was so narrow that his tail touched the water.

By this time, several of the other mother whales had come up. What was to be done! Suddenly Sharp Ears' mother seemed to have an idea. Swimming near her baby, she threw her tail out of the water, and with the flat of it gave Sharp Ears a terrific blow on the end of his nose. So strong was her tail and so severe was this slap that it actually pushed her baby's body off the ice and into the water. Sharp Ears' life was saved.

After the little whale was safe again, the gam started on. As the whales traveled, they passed many more icebergs, many of them larger than tall buildings. One of these huge floating mountains of ice was twenty-eight miles long!

A few days later, the whales passed Cape Horn and were in the Pacific Ocean. Here they met many severe storms. Strong winds came up often and unexpectedly. When these winds blew and the waves were high, the whales sounded and swam along many feet below the surface where there were no waves. Steadily they continued up the western coast of South America. Sharp Ears did not know where the whales were going, but his mother did. They were on a trip which would take them entirely around the world.

On Your Own

1. How did Sharp Ears escape from the killer whale? Why did he need help to get off the iceberg?

2. Make a list of things you learned about whales. You may wish to find out more about whales in an encyclopedia and add to your list. Here is a beginning.

   Whales swim long distances.

3. List on paper the words at the left below. Beside each word write the meaning that goes with it.

   (a) blubber   a herd, or school, of whales
   (b) gam   the fat of whales
   (c) calves   a floating mountain of ice
   (d) squid   dived toward the bottom of the sea
   (e) iceberg   young whales
   (f) sounded   a sea animal

Pegleg and the Whale

By BILL AND ROSALIE BROWN

Who was looking for the biggest whale in the whole wide world? It was Pegleg, the biggest whaler, of course. Can you guess what they did when they met? In a tall tale, anything can happen!

Pegleg Pete was a sailor man. He wore a big black patch over his left eye and a long black nightcap on his head. His wooden leg went thump! thump! while he paced the quarterdeck and then he'd stop and look out over the ocean through a long brass spyglass. He was looking for the biggest whale in the whole wide world.

"I'm the toughest, I'm the meanest, I'm the saltiest, I'm the biggest, I'm the orneriest whaler on the seven seas!" Pegleg roared. And when he roared like that and pulled his long red whiskers, the crew all ran and hid below decks.

Pegleg Pete sailed and he sailed looking for the biggest whale in the world. Then, down in the Indian Ocean, the lookout up in the crow's nest called out:

"Thar she bloooooooooows!"

"Whar away?" Pegleg roared.

"In front of yer nose!" the lookout said.

Pegleg hauled out the first joint of his spyglass and then he hauled out the second joint of his spyglass and he looked in front of his nose. The whale was blowing a fountain of steam into the air.

"Too little!" Pegleg roared. "He's only as big as a house!"

So they sailed and they sailed five more times around the world. Pegleg's wooden leg went thump! thump! thump! as he paced the quarterdeck. Then they came to the Bay of Biscay. Once more the lookout called:

"Thar she blooooooooooows!"

"Whar away?"

"In front of yer nose!"

Pegleg pulled out the first joint of his spyglass and then he hauled out the second joint of his spyglass and then he hauled out the third and last joint of his spyglass and he looked in front of his nose.

There he was, the biggest whale in the world. He was as big and round as a mountain and he spouted water and steam like a volcano. When he slapped the water with his tail, it sounded like thunder.

Pegleg looked at the whale again when they came closer. "Well, hang my red beard!" Pegleg roared in a voice of thunder. "I do believe that whale's got sea fever!" The whale was

Ka...ka...ka...CHOOOooooooo

snorting and blowing and his eyes were red and watery.

Just then the lookout yelled down a loud warning: "Look out, Cap'n Pegleg, that whale's going to sneeze!"

Pegleg roared to the crew: "Look out, he's going to sneeze!" The crew yelled, "He's going to sneeze!" And everybody hung on to the ropes.

The whale wrinkled up his face and wrinkled up his nose. His tail went up in the air. Then his tail came down with a splash and he went "Ka . . . ka . . . ka . . . CHOOOOOOoooooo!" Only, a million times bigger than anybody ever sneezed before.

The wind from that sneeze blew Pegleg's wooden leg out from under him but he hung on

to the ropes with his hands. His black nightcap went flying through the air. His brass spyglass went flying through the air. And the ship was blown seven hundred leagues north.

When the ship finally stopped, Pegleg looked out in front of his nose. And there was the whale again, blowing his nose and staring right at the ship with red and watery eyes. The biggest whale in the world had followed them all the way.

"He wants some medicine!" the lookout shouted from the crow's nest. "He wants it for his sea fever."

"Roll him out a barrel of aspirin!" Pegleg shouted to the crew. They rolled out a barrel

of aspirin and the whale swallowed it in one single swallow. Then he wrinkled up his face and he wrinkled up his nose and the lookout just started to yell, "He's going to sn . . . ." when the whale went "Ka . . . ka . . . ka . . . CHOOOOOO-ooooooo!"

So the whale blew the ship up to the North Pole among the icebergs and Pegleg got his ears frozen stiff. The crew threw him a barrel of molasses this time but he just sneezed some more. Then he blew the ship clear down to the Caribbean Sea and Pegleg got his nose sunburned. Then he blew the ship up to Nantucket Sound and

Pegleg could see his own little white house on the shore.

"Give him more medicine!" Pegleg roared to the crew.

"Aye, aye, sir," they said and rolled out the last barrel on the ship.

It was a big barrel of pepper. It rolled right into the whale's mouth and the pepper burned his throat and tickled his nose. He wrinkled up his face and he let go with the most powerful sneeze ever recorded in the whole wide world.

Pegleg tried to grab a rope but he missed. He went flying through the air with his red beard flowing behind him like a comet and he passed over the beach and he sailed right through the window of his own little white house and landed plop! right in his own bed. Pegleg pulled the covers up over his head.

"I'm the toughest and the meanest and the saltiest and the orneriest whaler on the seven seas," he muttered to himself. "But I'll never ever go whaling again as long as I live!"

On Your Own

1. What do you think each of these whaling expressions means?
   (a) "Thar she blooooooooooows!"
   (b) "Whar away?"
   (c) "In front of yer nose!"

2. What kind of whaler did Pegleg think he was? Do you agree with him? What did the crew do when Pegleg roared in a voice of thunder?

3. You have read two different kinds of stories about whales. Which could have happened? Which is a tall tale and could not have happened? Perhaps you would like to write a whale story of your own.

A DRAGON-FLY

By ELEANOR FARJEON

When the heat of the summer
Made drowsy the land,
A dragon-fly came
And sat on my hand;
With its blue jointed body,
And wings like spun glass,
It lit on my fingers
As though they were grass.

The Golden Tombo

By H. TOM HALL

In Japan, boys and girls love nature and like to collect things, just as you do. Here is a story of Toru and a strange and beautiful insect.

Toru's Summer

In the crowded country of Japan, on one of the many small farms, a young boy named Toru lives with his father, mother, and baby sister. Their home is a cheerful thatched-roof house at the edge of the rice paddies.

During the warm summer months yellow flowers grow from the straw roof, and swallows sing their morning song.

Each year as these signs of warm weather appear, Toru's father and farmers all over

Japan start the hard work of planting and cultivating the rice. For the schoolchildren the coming of warm weather brings other thoughts. It means vacation time has come at last.

One summer morning, on the last day of school, Toru got up earlier than usual. The sun was shining on the paper walls, lighting every corner of the room. Toru had rolled his Japanese bed, put it on the shelf, and had just slipped into his black school uniform when his mother called him to breakfast. He hurriedly ate his fried rice and egg. Then he grabbed his white schoolbag, slid open the door, and waved good-by to his parents. As he dashed off to school, Toru's mother and father smiled, for they knew how important this last day was to their son.

Toru had not gone very far when he met his three friends, Horiuchi-san, Watanabe-san, and Nita-san. After the boys had all greeted one another by saying, *"Ohayo gozaimas,"* which means "good morning," they continued down the path to school. Each was carrying his canvas schoolbag and a lunch-box of cold rice tied in a brightly colored piece of cloth.

Soon other children joined the four boys, all of them anxious to be on time.

Near the end of the day, when the lessons had been completed, the teacher asked the class, "What shall we do for our summer project?" The children gave suggestions to make and collect many different things, but they finally all agreed that the best idea was to catch insects. The girls talked about the beautiful *chochos*, butterflies, they could catch, and the boys talked of catching *semi*, cicadas, and *tombos*, dragonflies. Each boy and girl boasted that when school started again, he or she would have the best collection or the most interesting insects.

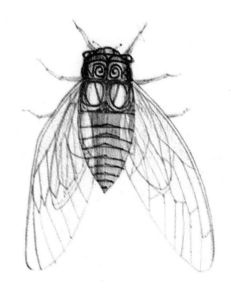

On the way home Toru was very excited about the summer vacation and the wonderful collection of insects he was going to have. He even stopped at the neighborhood store to get bottles to hold his bugs and bamboo strips to build cages.

When Toru arrived home with his armload of boxes, bottles, and strips of wood, he put them on a shelf in a corner of the room.

That evening Toru's father spoke to him. "Toru-san, in the past summers when the work in the rice paddies became too much for me, your mother has helped me. This year she has your baby sister to care for, so I must ask you to work beside me in the fields."

Toru thought of all the tombos and the other insects he had planned to catch. But now, working in the fields would leave no time for his project. Toru said after a moment, "Father, I will work very hard, and we will have a fine crop of rice this year."

The following day Toru joined his father in the rice paddies. The ox pulled while Toru's father guided the plow, and Toru followed behind gathering up the stones and weeds. There was much work before planting the rice.

Every day when the sun came up Toru and his father would start to work. They fixed the dirt and stone walls, and the little dams that control the water used to flood the paddies. They turned the earth and spread the fertilizer. And always there were weeds to be pulled!

After the rice grains were planted, the dams were opened and the water allowed to flood the paddies. Finally the young green rice plants began to appear, looking very much like grass. The young plants then had to be gently dug up and replanted in neat rows.

The next job was to put old broken umbrellas in the fields. The breeze would blow the strips of wood and torn paper, frightening away all the hungry crows and other birds. Yes, the umbrellas made fine scarecrows, and protected the rice plants.

One day as Toru and his father were taking the oxcart to town for fertilizer, they passed Nita-san, Watanabe-san, and Horiuchi-san chasing some insects. For the first time since Toru had started to work he thought of the summer project. He would have no insects to show the teacher and the class when school started in the fall, and they would surely think that he had not tried. Toru thought of how his classmates

might laugh at him, for they would have wonderful things to show. He wondered if his teacher would think that he had been lazy.

All that day Toru felt very sad, but he went right on with his work, never complaining to his father or mother.

Toru saw his friends many times after that. They were always catching or playing with insects. At the pond he saw them with their tombo poles. These were made from a long length of bamboo, coated at the end with sticky sap.

They held the pole out to the tombos, or dragonflies, until one touched the pole and stuck fast. The little four-winged insect would then be put into a small cage with other tombos. Sometimes Nita-san tied a string around a tombo's middle and let it fly around over his head like a small shining kite. Toru felt that this must not be very pleasant for the tombo, having a string tied to him, but to the boys it seemed like great fun.

They caught more and more tombos, and soon their cage was filled with buzzing insects of all colors.

Toru would often look at his empty bottles and the strips of bamboo which were never made into cages, and he would dream about the collection he might have had. Yes, it was nice to dream, but dreams could not be shown to his teacher or class friends.

Toru's Tombo

On the last day of vacation Toru was spreading the rice grain on mats to dry in the sun. He had been thinking about the next day and his proud classmates showing their projects. It would not be a happy day for poor Toru.

Then, as he turned, Toru saw something from the corner of his eye that made him gasp with surprise. A tombo was sitting very still on a lone stalk of rice. This was not an ordinary tombo, for it glowed with a bright gold color and was so large. "This surely is the biggest tombo anyone has ever seen," thought Toru. Somehow, without a net or a pole, he must try to catch this tombo.

Suddenly an idea came to Toru. He crept closer and closer, then took off his hat and held it above the insect. Just as it seemed ready to fly away, Toru leaped, trapping the Golden Tombo in his hat. It was his; the Golden Tombo was now his!

In the excitement of catching his prize, Toru quickly forgot the long months of work when there had been no time for his project.

Toru's father was very puzzled when his son dashed by. His mother was also quite confused and frightened by the large flapping bug Toru held up for her to see. Even the baby looked startled.

Toru wasted no time. He ran straight to his room, put his prize in one of his mother's baskets, and gathered the things he needed to make a cage. The roof was taken from an old lantern. A base was cut from

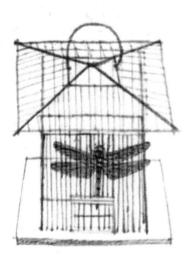

a pine board, and the bars were fashioned from the long thin strips of bamboo. Toru used rice paste to fasten most of the cage together and a few pieces of thin wire to make the corners stronger and to hang the small door.

When Toru finally finished, he had a very special cage for his very special tombo. The door was safely tied shut, and Toru went to bed knowing that he too would have something to show at school.

The children were all excited on the first day of school, and anxious to show what they had done over the summer months. As they reached the front door carrying their cloth-covered projects, each would stop to remove his sandals. In Japan it is not polite to wear any type of shoes inside a building.

When everyone had arrived, the teacher welcomed the class and began to look at their summer projects.

There were many beautiful butterflies and several large jars of fireflies. Most of the boys had collections of tombos. Every type and color of insect was represented, and most of them were displayed in cages or glass-covered boxes. There were bottles filled with tiny moths and covered cages full of cicadas which made loud squealing noises.

The teacher looked at each project and seemed pleased with the summer's work of her class. Mochi-san showed her a collection of beetles, and Hosogi-san his fine collection of spiders. The silkworm moths and empty cocoons that Katoh-san showed were very interesting. Finally the teacher had looked at everyone's project but Toru's. He held his breath as she looked first at his Golden Tombo and then at him.

Much to Toru's surprise the teacher said that his was the best summer project. She explained that the Golden Tombo was the finest she had ever seen, but the reason she chose Toru was because he had helped his father all summer without complaining. "Toru-san, you should be very proud," said the teacher. And Toru was proud.

That day he walked slowly home from school thinking about what the teacher had said.

When Toru crossed the rice paddy, he stopped at the spot where he had first seen the tombo sitting very still on a lone stalk of rice. Opening the door, Toru gently lifted the beautiful creature from the cage. It hesitated for a moment, and then, with four glasslike wings moving almost too fast to see, it sailed off into the distance, until Toru could only see the glitter of the sun shining on his Golden Tombo.

On Your Own

1. Find in the story the meanings of these Japanese words. Write on paper each word and its meaning.
   (a) chochos
   (b) semi
   (c) tombos
   (d) Ohayo gozaimas

2. Look up *rice* in an encyclopedia. Why is rice so important in Japan? List in order the things Toru and his father did to help the rice grow.

3. Why do you think Toru did not complain about working that summer? What would you have done?

4. How did Toru's dream come true? Why do you think he let the Golden Tombo go?

5. Make a list of insects that were in the children's collections. Be ready to tell about a collection you have made.

SWIFT

By AKINOBÔ

The dragon-fly,
Swift to the distant mountain,
Swift to return.

SPLINTER

By CARL SANDBURG

The voice of the last cricket
across the first frost
is one kind of good-by.
It is so thin a splinter of singing.

ONE GUESS

By ROBERT FROST

He has dust in his eyes and a fan for a wing,
A leg akimbo with which he can sing,
And a mouthful of dye stuff instead of a sting.

Weighing the Long-Nosed Giant

Retold by S. Y. Lu Mar

Tsao Tsong, a clever boy, said it would be a simple thing
to weigh the long-nosed giant.   See if you agree.

A Problem for a Wise One

"Ho   Ling!"   called   Tsao   the South Yard to see the long-
Tsong.   "Come on!   Let's go to   nosed giant!"

"What's that?" Ho Ling asked, running out from the courtyard to join his friend.

"That's an elephant," Tsao Tsong explained. "It's the biggest animal that walks on four legs. Haven't you ever seen its picture?"

"No," Ho Ling said. "What's it like? Is it dangerous?"

"Oh, no," Tsao Tsong said. "It is big but very tame. My father, the Prime Minister, says it is a present from the Kingdom to the South."

Pulling their robes up to their knees, the two boys took a short cut, rushing through a thick bamboo grove. When they reached the yard, they saw a crowd there already.

"Wait," Tsao Tsong whispered, pulling his friend's robe. "There is my father, there, with some of the court officials. No doubt, they, too, are here to see this giant. We must not disturb them." He led the way behind some bushes.

"Ha! This animal looks exactly like the one in the picture," Tsao Tsong whispered.

"See its long nose, the pointed tusks and the four sturdy legs."

Ho Ling, wide-eyed and open-mouthed, was much impressed by the awesome sight of the giant animal. As they watched, the elephant lifted a huge teak log with his powerful nose and held it tightly against his tusks. He then set it gently down on another spot, exactly where his trainer told him.

"Ay ya! Wonderful!" the two boys exclaimed. They saw the officials nod their heads, astonished that man could change a fierce giant beast into a work animal.

"This is a very useful animal, indeed," the Prime Minister said, well pleased. "But can anyone tell me a way to learn his weight?"

There was silence, for nobody had the answer.

The Prime Minister frowned. "Speak up, you learned men! Is there none among you here wise enough to give me the answer to my question?"

Again there was nothing but silence.

"This is a problem for a wise one," the Prime Minister said. "And as a reward to the person who supplies the answer, I shall send him as my messenger with a return gift to our good friends in the Kingdom to the South."

This set Tsao Tsong's mind working hard and fast. There must be a way to weigh the giant beast, he told himself thoughtfully. Could he win the trip south? While he listened to their discussion, his mind worked swiftly.

An elderly man now stepped forward. Facing the Prime Minister, he said, "Nothing should be impossible for our all-wise Prime Minister. You could easily order an ironworker to build a huge balance scale, big enough and strong enough to weigh this giant."

There were sounds of agreement among his colleagues, but the Prime Minister remained unimpressed. "Even if such a balance scale could be built, how could we safely lift such a giant weight?"

Someone suggested that a thousand-year-old tree should be strong enough.

The Prime Minister shook his head. "Such an aged tree might be deep in a valley or up on a mountain top."

Tsao Tsong forgot himself and burst into loud laughter.

"Who is laughing?" the Prime Minister asked in an angry voice.

Tsao Tsong realized that he had been acting improperly. He left his hiding place, straightened himself, and stepped forward politely.

The Prime Minister frowned that his son should be the one to blame. "Don't you know that to laugh at an elder's statements is very impolite?"

"Yes, *Bah Ba*," the boy answered. "But I wasn't laughing at anyone's statement. I believe a balance scale even with a metal chain is likely to break under the great weight of such a giant. In my mind I pictured this huge animal rolling down the mountainside. That made me laugh."

The Prime Minister's severe face changed slowly. He leaned back, chuckling at his son's imagination.

His amusement gave Tsao Tsong a new assurance. "If you please, *Bah Ba*, I believe I know how to weigh this giant. It is simple . . . if you will let me do it."

Now the whole courtyard roared with laughter at the boy's suggestion.

"It couldn't possibly be that easy, my son," his father said. "One tusk alone is heavier than your whole body."

"True, *Bah Ba*. But I believe I know a way to find the answer. If you will let me try, I shall, before sunset, present *Bah Ba* with the exact weight of this long-nosed giant. All I need is a dozen workmen and a boat big enough to carry the huge beast."

The Prime Minister studied the boy a moment, then nodded his head. "You shall have what you want, my son," he said. "You have spoken out boldly in front of your elders. Now make good your promise. If you fail, however, you must apologize to each one of these officials for your unmannerly actions. You will find us at the palace."

Tsao Tsong knew he had made a big promise, and his heart pounded with fear that the animal might not obey.

"Can you control the giant beast?" he asked the driver, who was called a mahout. "Will he do what you tell him?"

"Indeed, he is trained to obey," the mahout assured the boy. "In our country, he is a valuable work animal."

Finding the Answer

A few moments later Tsao Tsong and Ho Ling were riding happily on the elephant's back, seated behind the mahout. The elephant lumbered toward the river bank. The boys rode in state and felt like princes of the Kingdom to the South.

At the river bank, they found a large boat at its landing. Also the twelve workmen waited there, as ordered.

Both Ho Ling and the elephant driver were puzzled. They could not guess what Tsao Tsong planned to do, but they did not have long to wait. Tsao Tsong stepped onto the boat and asked the driver to bring the elephant on board. After some trouble, the mahout got the elephant to cross the gangplank onto the boat. Immediately, the heavy weight of the animal forced the boat much lower down into the water.

Tsao Tsong bent over the side of the boat and watched the water line. Then, with a knife, he carved a mark first on one side and then on the other. When that was completed, he told the mahout to take the elephant ashore.

Everyone present remained puzzled. But Tsao Tsong seemed to know exactly what he was doing.

"Now, bring rocks as large as you can carry," Tsao Tsong ordered the twelve workmen. "Load them in the boat until I tell you to stop."

As the men loaded the boat with rocks, Tsao Tsong bent over each side and watched carefully the marks he had

carved. He gave orders where to place the rocks, some on the left side and some on the right. The twelve workmen, much puzzled, continually exchanged wondering glances. When the boat was well loaded, Tsao Tsong called out, "Stop!"

"Now, we need a balance scale." One was quickly brought forth, and a rock was tied with a strong rope and hooked on to one end of the scales. Two men slid the weight on the beam of the scales until there was a perfect balance.

Each rock was thus weighed and its weight recorded. When all the rocks were weighed, Tsao Tsong added all the weights together.

Waving the piece of paper triumphantly, he shouted, "Here is the weight of the long-nosed giant!" Then he rushed to the palace to find his father.

In the middle of a meeting with his officials, the Prime Minister noticed the presence of his son. "Don't tell me that you have already weighed the huge elephant!"

"Yes, *Bah Ba*," Tsao Tsong said, and he presented the slip of paper.

"The weight of this long-nosed giant is 5988 catties." The Prime Minister read the figure aloud in astonishment. "But how do we know it is correct? Tell us how you arrived at this figure."

"*Bah Ba*, as I said before, it was very simple," Tsao Tsong explained. "At first, a boat was loaded with the elephant. Its weight caused the boat to submerge to a certain depth. Where the surface of the water touched, the boat was marked. Later, large rocks were used.

Enough rocks were placed in the boat so that the marks again just touched the surface of the water. When I weighed all the rocks, I arrived at the figure of 5988 catties. This figure should be the same as the weight of this animal."

"That sounds very reasonable, my son," the Prime Minister decided, while his officials nodded their heads in astonished approval. "And you have earned the reward I promised. You shall accompany the men who go south next month. There you will see many long-nosed giants and other marvels, unknown to us."

On Your Own

1. Do you agree with Tsao Tsong that it was a simple thing to weigh the long-nosed giant? Why? How did he do it? Tell the story in pictures or words.

2. List on paper the words at the left below. Beside each word write the meaning that goes with it.

(a) mahout

(b) catties

(c) teak

a tall East Indian tree

an elephant driver

measures of weight, each around 1⅓ pounds

THE FOUR FRIENDS

By A. A. MILNE

Ernest was an elephant, a great big fellow,
    Leonard was a lion with a six-foot tail,
George was a goat, and his beard was yellow,
    And James was a very small snail.

Leonard had a stall, and a great big strong one,
    Ernest had a manger, and its walls were thick,
George found a pen, but I think it was the wrong one,
    And James sat down on a brick.

Ernest started trumpeting, and cracked his manger,
    Leonard started roaring, and shivered his stall,
James gave the huffle of a snail in danger
    And nobody heard him at all.

Ernest started trumpeting and raised such a rumpus,
    Leonard started roaring and trying to kick,
James went a journey with the goat's new compass
    And he reached the end of his brick.

Ernest was an elephant and very well-intentioned,
    Leonard was a lion with a brave new tail,
George was a goat, as I think I have mentioned,
    But James was only a snail.

Thinking It Through

1. Here are main ideas from the six stories. Write each main idea. Beside it, write the name of the main character and the title of the story.
   (a) He had to learn for himself.
   (b) He solved a puzzling problem.
   (c) He needed help to win a strange race.
   (d) He tried to catch the biggest whale.
   (e) He met with danger on a long journey.
   (f) His dream came true in an unusual way.

2. Pretend that you were a big-game hunter on the African veldt driving the Honkebeest. How would you describe the race with Raffy? What other animals did you see?

3. In what way were Raffy, Tsao Tsong, and Toru alike? In what way was Tarnish's adventure like Sharp Ears'? Prove your points by reading from the stories.

4. The elephant weighed 5988 catties. How much is this in pounds? Perhaps you can work this out with your teacher's help in class.

5. The map in this story shows the Panama Canal. Ships sailing from the Atlantic Ocean to the Pacific Ocean save time by going through the Panama Canal. Why didn't Sharp Ears' gam go through the Canal? Trace on a globe or map the route the whales took.

6. Which animal in these stories did you like best? Find out more about it in encyclopedias or animal books. Plan a talk about it.

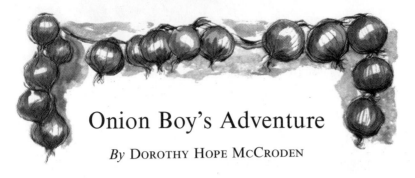

Onion Boy's Adventure

By DOROTHY HOPE McCRODEN

Can you think how hard it would be to keep on being kind when people are not kind in return? Peter did it! Can you imagine how anyone could find an exciting adventure with strings of onions? Peter did it!

Long ago, in a country far away, a young peasant boy lived with his uncle in a poor hut in the woods. The boy's name was Peter.

Every morning just as the sun was creeping over the horizon, Peter and his uncle would get up, put on their faded smocks, eat a bit of bread, and go to work in the onion fields near their hut. Every night they would plod wearily home through the twilight, eat a bit of bread and cheese, drink some goat's milk, and lie down on their straw mats to sleep.

"Will it always be like this?" asked Peter one day when he had been harvesting onions.

"Will I never go out into the world and have adventures?"

His uncle was silent for a moment. "I don't know about adventures," he replied slowly, "but I think you are old enough even now to go to market by yourself. Tomorrow you shall carry in a load of onions."

Peter's eyes shone with joy. "Oh, thank you, Uncle!" he cried. He could scarcely believe his good fortune, and that night he slept hardly a wink. In the morning, while they ate their breakfast, the uncle told Peter, "Go straight to the onion man at the vegetable market. When he has paid you, come directly home."

"Oh, I will," said Peter. "I'll hurry home and tell you about my exciting adventures."

The onions for the market were tied together in long strings. Peter's uncle hung rows and rows of them around the boy's neck. "Have a good time," the uncle said. "And don't forget to be kind to every-one you meet."

"I won't forget," promised Peter. And then he started on his way. It was still early in the day, and the village roofs were golden with light from the rising sun. The road stretched out in-vitingly before Peter's feet, winding away between two low green hills.

For half an hour, perhaps, he walked along with only rabbits and birds to keep him company. Then, just ahead, around a bend in the road, he saw an old woman coming out of a cottage door, carrying a heavy basket on her arm. "She, too, must be on the way to market," thought Peter. "I'll hurry and catch up with her. It will be pleasant to have a companion, and perhaps I can help carry her basket."

He quickened his steps, and called, "Good mother, hello! Are you headed for market?"

The woman turned quickly to look at him, lost her balance, and sat down with a thud in the middle of the road. Her ker-chief went flying off her head and landed in a ditch. The basket, still clutched in her

hand, was overturned, and potatoes rolled helter-skelter over the road.

"Oh, I'm sorry!" cried Peter. "Let me help you." He stretched out his hand to the old woman.

"Don't touch me, you wicked boy!" she screamed. "Scaring folks out of their wits!" She scrambled to her feet.

Peter began to gather up the potatoes for her, putting them in the pockets of his smock, since she still held the basket.

When the old woman saw what he was doing, she shook her fist at him and shouted, "Thief! Thief!"

Hurriedly, Peter placed the potatoes in the woman's basket. "They're all there, I think," he said. "Now I will say good day to you and be on my way."

"Be off with you!" muttered the old woman.

"I only meant to be kind," thought Peter as he journeyed on his way.

The winding road twisted its way through the hills. Peter had been walking for some time now with the sun warm on his face. He began to feel thirsty, and just then spied a well in a cottage dooryard. A girl was playing with her dog beside it. "Surely she will give me a drink," he thought.

He spoke to the girl. "Hello," he said. "May I please have a drink from your well?"

The girl looked at him and laughed. "How ridiculous you look!" she said. "Go away, onion boy. I hate onions."

"I'm taking them to market," explained Peter. "I've come a long way. May I drink?"

The girl placed her hands on her waist. "Go away, you dirty boy!" she ordered. She looked down at her dog. "Get him, Rex. Get him!" she said.

The dog leaped at Peter and tore his smock, but the boy managed to fight him off. Then he hurried on down the road, the onion strings streaming out behind him. After a while, he slowed down to catch his breath.

Now the day had really begun. Farmers' carts began to pass Peter as he traveled on. People moved about in the fields. Children waved at Peter. "Soon I shall be in the village," he decided.

After a while Peter noticed a white-haired man walking slowly in front of him, leaning on a stick. Just then, behind Peter, a wagon came clattering along at a great pace. The boy stepped aside to let it pass, but the old man with the stick was not so nimble. He tried to get out of the way of the horses, but as the wagon went by, a corner of it brushed against him, and the old man was knocked down. The wagon did not stop, but rattled on toward the village.

Peter began to run. "I'll help you!" he said, and held out his arms to the old man, pulling him to his feet. "Just lean on me," he commanded.

"How kind you are," said the old man. "My house is just over the hill. Will you help me home?"

"Of course. Just lean on me. I am strong," Peter assured him.

"Not too strong for that load you're carrying," the man said.

"Oh, this is nothing," Peter told him. "I'm going to market for my uncle. It's the first time I've been there alone, but I shall carry loads heavier than this before the harvest is over."

The old man nodded his head as they walked slowly on. At last they reached his house. "Now I'm all right," he said, sinking down on the doorstep. "Draw yourself a fresh drink from the well, and then sit down and rest a moment."

Peter dipped the bucket into the sparkling water and pulled up a refreshing drink. Oh, how good it was! And how pleasant it was to rest after his long walk!

The old man smiled at him. "My boy," he began, "you have been very good to me, and I wish to repay your kindness. If you will walk around to the back of the house, I think you will find something there that you can use."

Peter hesitated.

"Go ahead," said the old man.

Peter walked around to the back of the cottage, and there he stopped short, for he saw the most beautiful wheelbarrow that had ever been made. It was not large. It was not small. It was exactly the right size for Peter. It had flowers on it— flowers painted on the sides for decoration.

The boy turned to look at his friend, who had followed him around the house. "Do you like it?" the old man asked.

"It's wonderful," said Peter.

"And it's yours," his new friend told him. "It's no earthly good to me. Too small. But it will be just right for you. Here, let's get those onions off your neck so you can try it out."

"Oh, thank you!" exclaimed Peter. "Thank you very much!"

"And now off with you," said the old man. "It's time you were on your way to market."

Peter's heart beat quickly as he rolled the little wheelbarrow along the road. He could hardly wait to go home and tell his uncle about it.

Now the village was only a short distance away. But up ahead something was blocking the road. There seemed to be great confusion. People ran back and forth, horses jumped. Peter could hear shouting. He hurried forward.

There ahead of Peter was a sight such as he had never seen even in his dreams. A coach drawn by six frightened horses lay half on its side, in the ditch. Peter could see that an axle of the coach was broken. Men in splendid uniforms rushed about knocking into each other in the excitement. Farmers left their loaded carts and offered advice. Nearby was standing a beautiful woman. Peter stared at her and saw that it was the queen of his country.

And at this moment the royal lady began speaking to persons who stood near her. "Must I stand here all day?" she asked. "Will someone please take me to the village inn so I can rest while the coach is being fixed?"

"Your Majesty," a farmer said, "gladly would I drive you to the inn, but I have a load of cabbages on my wagon and have no room."

"The same would I," declared another, "but my horse is old and could not draw us both."

"We could send to the village for a carriage, but it will take time," suggested a courtier.

While the excuses were being made, a daring thought flashed through Peter's mind. Should

he speak? He looked down at the little wheelbarrow. Then he looked at the queen. "Your Majesty," he began hesitantly, "I have nothing but a wheelbarrow, but I am very strong. I could push you into the village. It is not far."

"Silence," commanded one of the red-coated men, frowning at the boy and his wheelbarrow.

"Such airs!" another one said. "Such boldness!"

"Hush," commanded the queen. "This lad is kind. Fetch me a pillow from the coach.

This wheelbarrow shall carry me to the village."

"Will someone please help me put these onions around my neck?" asked Peter. "I must get them to the market."

The queen laughed. "That would be too big a load for one so small. I will buy the onions, for the palace." She reached into her pocket and handed the boy a gold piece.

Peter gasped. It was more money than he had ever seen before. He swallowed hard and said, "It is too much."

"Nonsense," said the queen. "I must pay you for the ride, too, you know."

So the onions were placed in the royal coach, and the queen made herself comfortable in the wheelbarrow, and Peter pushed her down the road to the village. How careful he was to steer clear of stones! How strong and important he felt! "My queen needs me," the boy thought. "What a wonderful adventure I am having. And what a remarkable morning!"

The beautiful queen talked to Peter and asked him questions. He told her about his uncle and the hut in the woods. He told her about the potato woman, the girl and her dog, and the wonderful friend who had given him the wheelbarrow.

At last the journey was over. The queen alighted at the door of the inn. And there, to Peter's astonishment, with villagers staring at them, she bent down and kissed him. "As soon as the onion harvest is over," she said to the boy, "perhaps we can arrange to have you come to the palace as a royal page."

"Oh, Your Majesty, thank you, but I could not leave my uncle."

"Well, we shall see," said the queen. "We may need another gardener at the palace too. I shall send word to you and your uncle," she promised. And then she disappeared into the inn.

Like a boy in a dream, Peter turned around and started home. The wheelbarrow fairly skimmed over the rough village road. "What wonderful adventures one may have in the world," he said to himself. He began to walk faster so that he could get home and tell his uncle about his exciting journey.

On Your Own

1. What were the uncle's last words of advice? What happened when Peter followed this advice with:
   - (a) The potato woman
   - (b) The girl and her dog
   - (c) The kind old man
   - (d) The queen

2. Why is it not always easy to be kind? Should really kind people always expect kindness in return? What kind of rewards did Peter get? Do you think he would have been happy with only smiles and kind words from the queen? What is perhaps the best reward for being kind?

3. This story will make a fine play. On your paper make plans that show:
   - (a) What scenes you will have
   - (b) What people will be in each scene
   - (c) What the characters will do and say
   - (d) What "props" you will need

MOMOTARA

By ROSE FYLEMAN

Where did Momotara go,
With a hoity-toity-tighty?
He went to lay the giants low,
The wicked ones and mighty.

What did Momotara take?
His monkey, dog and pheasant,
Some dumplings and an almond cake,
Which made the journey pleasant.

How did Momotara fare
Upon the fearful meeting?
He seized the giants by the hair
And gave them all a beating.

What did Momotara bring?
Oh, more than you could measure:
A silver coat, a golden ring
And a wagon-load of treasure.

What did Momotara do?
He sat himself astride it;
The monkey pushed, the pheasant drew
And the little dog ran beside it.

The Woodcutter's Helper

By ALICE GEER KELSEY

This tale about a Hodja comes from Turkey. A Hodja was a man known for his clever mind and quick wit. See if the Hodja in this story made a wise decision.

High on a mountain trail, Nasr-ed-Din Hodja pulled his donkey to a sudden stop. The ring of an axe, the sound of a man's voice, and the tinkling of donkey bells told him there was companionship in this quiet, lonely spot.

Soon he came upon six donkeys pastured on some cleared land. On all sides were piles of wood cut into stove lengths. Nearby was a strong-armed man swinging an axe. The woodcutter stepped quickly back as a pine tree swayed, moaned, and fell to the ground. On a stump in the cool shade sat a neatly dressed man who clapped and cheered as the tree fell.

"Well done, my strong woodcutter!" shouted this second man who was not much more than half the size of the woodcutter. "That was a fine, big tree we cut. That will keep Siraj-ed-Din Bey warm many winter days. On to the next tree!"

Without looking at his companion, the woodcutter walked around an oak tree to decide where it should fall, took a strong hold on his axe handle, and started swinging just above the tree's roots.

Each time the woodcutter's axe bit into the tree, the little man on the stump would grunt.

The Hodja sat on his donkey, watching this strange performance—the strong man swinging the axe without a sound passing his lips while the sitting man kept up a steady flow of grunts, groans, and cheers. It was too much for the Hodja's curiosity.

"Why do you make all the noise while the other man does all the work?" he asked the trim little man.

"Oh, I am helping him," chattered the man. "He has agreed to cut thirty donkey loads of wood for Siraj-ed-Din Bey. Think what a job that would be for one man. I took pity on him and went into partnership with him. He swings the axe while I grunt and cheer to keep up his courage."

The Hodja watched the woodcutter who was saying nothing, but making the chips fly. "I think," said the Hodja thoughtfully, "it is the woodcutter's strong arms that give him courage."

The Hodja looked at the sun. It was growing late and he was

111

not finding the two men very lively company. The Hodja gave a low throaty "Ughr-r-r-," which started the donkey picking its careful way down the mountain trail toward home.

It was two weeks later that the Hodja came upon the two men of the mountaintop again. He was lingering about the court, just in case the Judge might need his advice about anything. It was amazing how often the Hodja's nimble wit could pull the Judge's sober wisdom out of a tangle. The two men of the mountaintop were arguing before the Judge. They moved their hands as fast as they moved their tongues.

"I earned every ghurush of it myself," the big woodcutter was saying. "I did every stroke of the cutting of thirty donkey loads of wood for Siraj-ed-Din Bey. I loaded the wood onto the donkeys. I drove them to Siraj-ed-Din Bey's house, unloaded every stick of the wood alone, and went back to the mountain for more loads."

"He forgets!" the trim little man of the stump broke in. "He forgets how I cheered him at his

work. I had a grunt for every swing of his axe, and a cheer for every falling tree. I earned a goodly share of the money which Siraj-ed-Din Bey made the mistake of paying entirely to the woodcutter."

The Judge looked helpless. He had never met just such a case before. There was nothing in his law books about this kind of argument. He was heartened to see the familiar figure of Nasr-ed-Din Hodja making his way through the crowd.

"I turn this case over to my able assistant, Nasr-ed-Din Hodja Effendi," said the Judge. "Repeat your stories to the Hodja."

Both talking at once, the woodcutter and his self-appointed helper told their stories. The Hodja listened, nodding wisely, till both men had talked themselves silent.

Then the Hodja beckoned smartly to a nearby court attendant.

"Bring me the money tray," said the Hodja.

The tray was brought. The crowd pressed nearer to see what was going to happen.

"Give me the money, good woodcutter, the money Siraj-ed-Din Bey paid you for the thirty donkey loads of wood."

"But it is my money," pleaded the woodcutter. "I sweated and worked for every ghurush of it while this man just sat in the shade and made strange sounds."

"The money, please," repeated the Hodja, holding out

his hand for the bag. Unwillingly, the woodcutter passed over the money bag while the little man of the stump drew nearer, his eyes greedily aglitter.

One by one, the Hodja took the coins from the bag and rang them out on the money tray, talking to the man who was claiming a share. "Do you hear that? Do you like the sound? Isn't that a cheery ring?"

The little man nodded, drawing so close that his nose almost touched the ringing coins.

The last ghurush had left the bag and had made its cheerful ring on the money tray. The big woodcutter moaned to see his hard-earned pay in danger. The little helper grinned to see so much money so near.

"You heard it all?" the Hodja asked the little man.

He nodded hungrily.

"Every ghurush of it?" asked the Hodja.

The little man nodded again.

"Then you have had your pay." The Hodja began to sweep the money back into the bag. "The sound of the money is proper pay for the sound of working."

The Hodja handed the full money bag to the smiling woodcutter, saying, "And the money is proper pay for the work."

On Your Own

1. Do you think the Hodja made a fair and wise decision? Why? Would you have made a different decision? Why?

2. List on paper the following: *woodcutter, Hodja, little man.* Beside each write the two words from the list below which describe that person.

lazy	clever	trusting
wise	hard-working	dishonest

3. Tell the story in pictures or words.

Chanticleer and the Fox

By GEOFFREY CHAUCER (*Adapted by* BARBARA COONEY)

Have you ever wished that animals could talk? They do in this story! Watch for the wisdom that the rooster and the fox are passing on to you.

Once upon a time a poor widow, getting on in years, lived in a small cottage beside a grove which stood in a little valley. This widow, about whom I shall tell you my tale, had patiently led a very simple life since the day her husband died. By careful management she was able to take care of herself and her two daughters.

She had only three large hogs, three cows, and also a sheep called Molly.

Her bedroom was blackened with smoke, as was her kitchen in which she ate many a scanty meal. She was never sick from overeating. Her table was usually set with only white and black—milk and dark bread, of which there was no shortage—and sometimes there was meat and an egg or two, for she was, as it were, a kind of farm woman.

She had a yard, fenced all around with sticks, in which she had a rooster named Chanticleer. For crowing there was none his better in all the land. His voice was merrier than the

115

merry organ that plays in church, and his crowing from his resting place was more trustworthy than a clock. His comb was redder than the setting sun and turreted like a castle wall; his bill was black and shone like jet, and his legs and toes were sky-blue. His nails were whiter than a sea shell, and his feathers were like burnished gold.

Now besides this fine rooster, there were seven hens, all colored very much like him. The hen with the prettiest throat was called fair Demoiselle Partlet. She was polite, proper, gay, and companionable, and she had conducted herself so well since the time that she was seven days old that, truly, she held the heart of Chanticleer all tightly locked. It was a great joy to hear them sing so sweetly together when the bright sun began to rise. For in those days, so I'm told, beasts and birds could talk and sing.

And so it happened, one day at dawn, as Chanticleer sat on his perch surrounded by the hens, that he began to groan in

his throat like a man troubled by his dreams. When Partlet heard him moaning this way she was frightened and said: "Dear heart, what is the matter that you groan in such a manner?"

And he answered saying: "Madam, I dreamed just now that I was in much danger. I dreamed that I was wandering up and down within our yard, when I saw a beast like a hound which tried to grab my body and would have killed me. His color was between yellow and red, and his tail and both ears were tipped with black, different from the rest of his fur. His snout was small, and his two eyes glowed. I almost died of

fear at the sight of him; doubt-less that's what caused my groaning."

"Go on!" she said. "Shame on you, you know I cannot love a coward, by my faith! Haven't you a man's heart and haven't you a beard? Be merry, Chanticleer. Do not fear dreams."

"Thank you, Madam Partlet," he said, "for your learned advice. I do say that when I see the beauty of your face all scarlet red about the eyes, my fears die away."

And with these words he flew down from the rafter, along with all the hens, for it was day. With a clucking he called them all to some grain which he found lying about the yard. He was as royal as a prince in his palace and was no longer afraid. He looked like a lion as he wandered up and down on his toes; he barely set foot to the earth.

Chanticleer, walking proudly, with the seven hens beside him, cast up his eyes at the bright sun. He crowed with a happy voice, "Listen how the happy birds sing, and how the fresh flowers grow; my heart is full of gaiety and joy."

But suddenly a sad event overtook him.

A fox, tipped with black, and full of sly wickedness, had lived in the grove three years. That same night he burst through the thicket into the yard where fair Chanticleer and the hens were in the habit of going. And this fox lay quietly in a bed of flowers until almost noon of that same day.

Partlet, with all her sisters nearby, lay merrily bathing in the sand, with her back to the sun, and the lordly Chanticleer sang more joyfully than the mermaid in the sea.

Now it happened that, as he cast his eyes upon a butterfly among the flowers, Chanticleer noticed the fox lying low. He had no wish to crow then, but at once cried, "Cok! cok!" and started up like a man frightened in his heart.

And he would have taken flight at once, if the fox had not said: "My dear sir, alas, where are you going? Are you afraid of me, your father's friend? The reason I came was only to listen to you sing. For, truly, you have as merry a voice as any angel in heaven. Your lordly father—God bless him—and also your courteous mother did me the great honor of visiting my house. Except for you I have never heard anyone who could sing as your father did in the morning. In order to make his voice stronger, he would close both his eyes. And he

would stand on his tiptoes and stretch forth his long slender neck. Now sing, sir! By my faith, let's see whether you can sing as well as your father."

Chanticleer began to beat his wings. He stood high on his toes and stretched his neck, closed his eyes, and crowed loudly. At once the fox jumped up, grabbed Chanticleer by the throat, and carried him toward the woods.

Alas, that Chanticleer flew down from the rafters! Alas, that Madam Partlet took no heed of dreams! And all this trouble came on a Friday.

Such a cry was never made as was made by all the hens in the yard when they saw Chanticleer captured. The poor widow and her two daughters heard the woeful cries of the hens and at once ran out of doors. They saw the fox going toward the grove, carrying away the rooster. "Help! Help! Woe is me! Look, a fox!" they screamed, and ran after him.

The cows, the sheep, and even the hogs, so frightened

were they by the shouting, ran after him, too. They ran so hard they thought their hearts would burst.

The neighbors' ducks quacked as if they were to be killed; and their geese, from fear, flew over the trees; the noise was so terrible that the bees crowded from their hive. It seemed that heaven would fall.

Now, good people, listen. In spite of his fear, the rooster in the fox's mouth spoke to the fox, saying, "Sir, if I were you, I would say, 'Turn back, you proud peasants! I have reached the edge of the wood now; the rooster shall stay here. In spite of you I will eat him, in faith, and not be long about it.' "

"In faith," the fox answered, "it shall be done." As soon as he spoke the words, the rooster nimbly broke away from his mouth and flew at once high into a tree.

When the fox saw that the rooster was gone, he said, "Alas! Oh, Chanticleer, alas! I have done you a bad turn. I frightened you when I grabbed you and took you out of the yard. But, sir, I did it with no wicked purpose. Come down and I shall tell you what I meant."

"Nay, then," said Chanticleer. "Never again shall you with your wicked flattery get me to sing with my eyes closed. For he who closes his eyes when he should watch, God brings him misfortune."

"No," said the fox, "but God brings misfortune to him who is so careless about his self-control as to chatter when he should hold his peace."

"See," said the widow as the fox crept into the grove, "that is the result of trusting in flattery."

And she marched with her flock back to the yard in the little valley.

On Your Own

1. Write a paragraph describing Chanticleer.

2. How did the fox manage to catch Chanticleer? What did the rooster do to show that he was quick-witted after all?

3. What are the words of wisdom that you learned from Chanticleer, the fox, and the widow?

TILLIE

By WALTER DE LA MARE

Old Tillie Turveycombe
Sat to sew,
Just where a patch of fern did grow;
There, as she yawned,
And yawn wide did she,
Floated some seed
Down her gull-e-t;
And look you once,
And look you twice,
Poor old Tillie
Was gone in a trice.
But oh, when the wind
Do a-moaning come,
'Tis poor old Tillie
Sick for home;
And oh, when a voice
In the mist do sigh,
Old Tillie Turveycombe's
Floating by.

Doctor Know-All

By WILHELM AND JACOB GRIMM (*Dramatized by* ETHEL L. HEINS)

When Crab, a poor woodcutter, hung out his sign, DOCTOR KNOW-ALL, a rich nobleman came to ask him to find some stolen money. Crab agreed. He and his wife went home with the nobleman. They sat down to a fine dinner. As the first servant came in, Crab whispered to his wife, "Look, Gretel, here is the first." He meant the first dish of food, but the servant, who was a thief, thought he meant the first thief. Through other mix-ups like this, Crab was finally able to find the stolen money. The nobleman thought he was a clever Doctor Know-All, but you might think he was just a lucky Crab.

Characters

CRAB, a poor woodcutter
GRETEL, his wife
DOCTOR
NOBLEMAN

FIRST SERVANT
SECOND SERVANT
THIRD SERVANT
FOURTH SERVANT

FIFTH SERVANT

SCENE 1:   A room in the home of a rich doctor.

CRAB *stands just inside the doorway, holding his hat in his hand.
The* DOCTOR'S *dinner is set out on the table: steaming soup, white
bread, a roast, frosted cakes, and a bowl of beautiful fruit.*

CRAB: Oh! If only I could be a doctor too, and eat such
    delicious dinners.
DOCTOR (*entering the room*): I see you have brought the
    wood. Here is your money, my good man. And good
    day to you.
CRAB (*walking to the door*): Oh, thank you, sir. (*He hesi-
    tates at the door, twisting his hat nervously.*) Uh, do
    you think I could learn to be a doctor, too?

DOCTOR: Oh, yes! No sooner said than done.

CRAB: Well, how would I go about it?

DOCTOR: First of all, you'll have to sell your two oxen and your cart. Second, with the money you must buy some fine clothes; also some medicine, pills, and whatever else you need for doctoring.

CRAB (*eagerly*): Yes, yes. Then what must I do?

DOCTOR: Well, third, you must buy an ABC book for yourself, the kind with a picture of a rooster in it. Last of all, you will have to paint a sign with the words I AM DOCTOR KNOW-ALL on it, and hang it over your door. That's all you really need. And now, good luck!

SCENE 2:   Inside Crab's house.

CRAB *sits at a desk, looking very wise and grand with his new eyeglasses, his long coat, and gold watch chain On the desk are the ABC book, several medicine bottles and boxes of pills, and a sign,* DOCTOR KNOW-ALL.

CRAB (*sighing*): Here I sit, all ready to be a doctor, but nobody comes. (*There is a knock at the door.* CRAB *jumps up, straightens his eyeglasses, and arranges his watch chain. Then he opens the door.*) Come in! Come in!

NOBLEMAN (*standing at the door, dressed in handsome, expensive clothes*): Are you Doctor Know-All?

CRAB: Yes! Yes!

NOBLEMAN: Then you're just the fellow I need! I've been robbed of a great deal of money. If you really know all, you will be able to tell me who has stolen it. Will you come along with me to my palace?

CRAB (*eagerly*): Yes, indeed I will. And my wife Gretel— may she come also?

NOBLEMAN: Certainly. But call her and let us go quickly. My coach is waiting.

SCENE 3: The nobleman's palace.

The stage is divided in half by a partition with a swinging door. To the left is the dining room, where a table is laid with rich-looking dishes and splendid foods. To the right is the servants' kitchen.

NOBLEMAN, CRAB, *and* GRETEL *enter the dining room.*

NOBLEMAN: I see that dinner is ready. Will you join me? (*He,* CRAB, *and* GRETEL *all sit down.*)

CRAB (*whispering to* GRETEL): Gretel, this will be a feast! There will be many dishes of food—you'll see. (FIRST SERVANT *enters with a dish of soup.* CRAB *points to it.*) Look, Gretel, here is the first. (*The servant is startled. He looks at the* DOCTOR *and returns to the kitchen.*)

FIRST SERVANT (*in kitchen, worried*): Oh, things will be bad for us now that our Master has brought this Doctor Know-All here. Do you know what? As soon as he set eyes on me, he told his wife that I was the first thief. (*The other servants gasp with fright. Then a bell sounds.*)

SECOND SERVANT (*very frightened*): There's the bell for the second dish! S-s-suppose he knows me too! (*He picks up a dish of food and takes it into the dining room.*)

CRAB (*glancing at* SECOND SERVANT, *and whispering to* GRETEL): See, Gretel, here comes the second. (SECOND SERVANT *hears him and rushes back to the kitchen.*)

SECOND SERVANT (*in kitchen*): Oh my goodness! He seemed to know I was the second thief as soon as he laid eyes on me. (*To* THIRD SERVANT): It's your turn now. We are out of luck! (THIRD SERVANT *nervously carries a dish into the dining room.*)

CRAB (*whispering to* GRETEL *as he sees* THIRD SERVANT *approach*): And that, Gretel, is the third. (THIRD SERVANT *sets down his dish hastily and dashes back to the kitchen.*)

THIRD SERVANT (*panting with fright*): We're done for! (*To* FOURTH SERVANT): You go in now and see what happens. (FOURTH SERVANT, *taking a covered dish, enters the dining room.*)

NOBLEMAN: Now, Doctor, we'll see if you know as much as you claim. Here is a servant with a covered dish. If you really know all about everything, you should be able to guess what is in the dish.

CRAB (*to himself, holding his head*): Oh, you poor old Crab! You're caught at last!

NOBLEMAN (*shouting with delight*): Good for you, Doctor! You've guessed it—there *is* a crab in the dish. (CRAB *grins.*) Now I'm sure you can find my stolen money too. (CRAB *holds his head again and groans.* FOURTH SERVANT *beckons to him from the doorway.*)

CRAB (*rising from the table*): Er—excuse me, please. (*He follows* FOURTH SERVANT *into the kitchen.*)

FIRST SERVANT (*very excited*): Oh, Doctor, you told your wife we were the thieves who stole our Master's money. Well, it's true! But we'll give it all back to him and reward you besides, if you'll promise not to tell.

CRAB: I'll promise, but only if you show me where the money is hidden.

SERVANTS: Oh yes, sir—here it is. (*They show* CRAB *the stolen money carefully hidden in a kitchen cupboard.* CRAB *returns to the dining room.*)

CRAB (*clearing his throat importantly*): Ha, ha! So you want to know what's happened to your money, my lord. Well, well! I'll have to search my book to find out about that. (*He sits down and opens the ABC book on his knees. He puts on his eyeglasses and, looking very wise, he begins to turn the pages over. He mumbles to himself*): I'll just look for the picture of the rooster. (*The servants meanwhile are holding the kitchen door open a crack and watching him curiously.*)

FIRST SERVANT: One of us should be in there to make sure the Doctor really keeps our secret. (FIFTH SERVANT *steals on tiptoe into the dining room and hides in a corner.*)

CRAB (*still turning the pages, looking for the picture of the rooster, and now impatiently shouting*): You nuisance! I know you're there and I'll find you yet!

FIFTH SERVANT (*rushing from the room and yelling*): He means me! Oh, oh! That man knows everything!

CRAB (*closing the book and smiling*): And now as to your stolen money, my lord. I can show just where it is. (*He leads the* NOBLEMAN *into the kitchen and opens the cupboard*). Here it is, every penny of it.

NOBLEMAN (*joyfully*): Well done, Doctor! I thank you indeed! (*He pulls out a bag of gold and gives it to* CRAB.) This is your reward, and I will tell all the world how clever you are. You will be famous as long as you live!

On Your Own

1. Below are four things that Crab said.
   (a) "Look, Gretel, here is the first."
   (b) "See, Gretel, here comes the second."
   (c) "Oh, you poor old Crab!"
   (d) "You nuisance!"

   Write (a), (b), (c), (d) on your paper. Beside each letter, write what Crab meant, then what the servants or nobleman thought he meant. Here is a beginning.

   (a) The first dish   The first servant

2. Choose the part of a character you like in the play. Study his part. Skim the play again for stage directions and the character's actions. Be ready to act out the part you choose.

THE KING OF CHINA'S DAUGHTER

By EDITH SITWELL

The King of China's daughter
So beautiful to see
With her face like yellow water, left
Her nutmeg tree.
Her little rope for skipping
She kissed and gave it me—
Made of painted notes of singing-birds
Among the fields of tea.
I skipped across the nutmeg grove,
I skipped across the sea;
But neither sun nor moon, my dear,
Has yet caught me.

The Little Empress

Retold by HELEN REEDER CROSS

It seemed that the little Empress had everything in the world to make her happy. But that was not true. It was quite by accident that she discovered two secrets that changed everything for her.

Homesick

Long ago, in the land of China, there was a young new Empress who was not happy. The sun shone brightly on the courtyard of the royal Palace of the Sun, but the new Empress

did not smile to see its bright-
ness. Instead, she sat weeping
in the shade of a mulberry tree.
Her three serving maids whispered behind their fans. "Perhaps if we dance she will stop
weeping," said one.

"She is so pretty when she
smiles," said another. "Yesterday she laughed aloud at the
playfulness of her pet monkey.
Her eyes sparkled and her
cheeks were like pink cherry
blossoms."

"I would not weep if I were
the new Empress of all China
and mistress of the Palace of the
Sun!" said a third maiden.

"Oh, but you might," the first
maid declared wisely. "If you,
too, were so young a bride. If
you, too, had left the home of
your childhood never to return."

She was right. Empress Si-
Ling-Shi was homesick. After
all, she was only fourteen years
old, and she missed her mother
and father. She missed her lively
brothers and sisters, too, and
the games that she had played
with them. She missed the lotus

pool at her old home, the moon gate, and the flowers in the courtyard of her father's house so far away.

Slowly, gracefully, the maids began the Dragon Dance which they hoped would amuse their mistress. They bowed and dipped and swayed like bright butterflies. The court musician picked a sad, sweet tune on his samisen. But the Empress' eyes were misted with tears.

"I, too, know the steps of the Dragon Dance," Si-Ling-Shi thought bitterly. She wept the harder because she knew that never again would she step its lovely figures. It would be unseemly for an Empress to dance.

Suddenly a hush fell over the courtyard. Someone whispered, "The Emperor is coming!"

Maids and musician bowed low, touching their foreheads to the ground. Si-Ling-Shi dried her eyes. It would never do for the Emperor to see her tears. Had not her Honorable Mother told her, "An Empress must forget her own happiness. It will be your duty to bring joy to the palace of your new husband."

The Emperor of all China approached. Toe-bells tinkled on his slippers. He was followed by his two ministers. Lifting the chin of his bride with one finger, the Emperor looked anxiously at her face. "What do I see, my peach blossom?" he asked. "Are these tears on your cheeks?" He pulled at his thin beard with his long pointed fingers.

Si-Ling-Shi tried hard to look gay and twinkling. After all, it was not the Emperor's fault that she was sad. He had done everything he could think of to make her happy in her new home. He had showered her with gifts—perfume and jewels, a singing bird in a bamboo cage, and a frolicsome monkey to make her laugh.

"Do not worry, my lord," she said. "It is just that the day is so long. You are busy with your court, while I have nothing to do from dawn to dark. The hours drag like lazy snails."

The Emperor frowned. "Something shall be done about this," he declared. "My bride must not dim her almond eyes with weeping. I shall order new dancing girls! Three that will put *these* unworthy three to shame. And a player to make music twice as sweet as his!" He pointed at the shivering musician impatiently.

"No! Do not send away these friends!" pleaded Si-Ling-Shi. "They are not at fault!"

The Emperor turned to his ministers. "Then I order you, my lords, to think of something that will amuse the Empress. Think of something so amusing that never again will I find her in tears. Tomorrow at noon I shall expect a plan to be ready."

The two men bowed low, casting anxious glances at each other. How could a homesick girl be kept from weeping? Especially when she already had everything in the world to make her happy?

Feeling sorry for them, Si-Ling-Shi said, "I do not need to be amused, Honorable Husband. Let the ministers think, instead, of something for me to *do* while you are at court. Something useful, perhaps."

Everyone looked startled. An Empress doing something useful? Why, it was unheard of! Empresses sat endlessly under mulberry trees, sipping tea and bowing graciously to all.

Si-Ling-Shi continued. "In my Honorable Father's house I was thought clever with my hands. I embroidered with delicate threads. Sometimes I painted birds on fine rice bowls."

"Well, well, we shall see," the Emperor said quickly, patting her on the shoulder as a child is patted. After all, his bride was still very young. She would get over such foolish notions in time. "But remember!" he said sternly to his ministers. "Have a plan at noon tomorrow!"

After the Emperor returned to his throne room Si-Ling-Shi nodded to her maids. "Dance for me again," she asked. "The exciting Tiger Dance. And do

not worry. I shall never again let the Emperor see my tears."

Magic in a Teacup

Scarcely had the girls begun to perform the lively figures of the Tiger Dance when a servant brought a tray. He set this before the Empress where she sat cross-legged under the mulberry tree. It was time for tea. Si-Ling-Shi, with the proper manners of the Tea Ceremony, poured for her maids, then for the musician, last for herself.

The tea was too hot to drink. Si-Ling-Shi sat looking at the pale gold liquid in her cup. In spite of the polite smile on her face, her heart was still heavy.

All at once, something fell into her tea with a splash. She jumped up quickly, spilling a little of the hot tea on her robe. It was her prettiest one, too—embroidered with great golden-brown chrysanthemums.

The maids sprang to help the Empress and to get her a fresh cup of tea.

"No, don't!" the Empress ordered them sharply. "Let me see what has fallen into the tea."

But it was nothing new or startling. Only a cocoon from the mulberry tree over her head. Every year, in the springtime, many such cocoons clung to the branches of mulberry trees all over China.

Yet, as she watched, something happened. The cocoon began to come apart in the hot tea. In a short time a delicate tangle of fine threads covered the liquid. The Empress was interested. She lifted the cocoon and all gently from her tea. The fine, shining strands floated in the air lightly. They were like pale gold threads. Si-Ling-Shi started to unwind the cocoon still more. She noticed that the fine hairs were strong and did not break, even though they looked very delicate.

Maids and musician sat watching their mistress. Tea,

tears, dancing were all forgotten. When Si-Ling-Shi was weary with unwinding the strand, one of the maids took a turn. This one cocoon seemed to have miles of thread wrapped round and round the sleeping worm in its center.

At last, in the Empress' lap there was a pile of shining fiber. "How beautiful it is!" Si-Ling-Shi exclaimed wonderingly. She continued, "What a lovely robe this thread would make if it could be woven into cloth. A robe fit for an Emperor!"

She caught her breath. Why not try it? The single strand was too slender, but why not twist several strands together? Then there would be a strong thread, thick enough for weaving into cloth. Only it would take many cocoons.

Jumping to her feet, and forgetful of an Empress' dignity, Si-Ling-Shi peered up into the mulberry tree. Yes, there were dozens of cocoons. In a twinkling she almost climbed up into the lower branches herself.

But the startled glances of her maids stopped her. "Here, sir," she ordered the court musician. "I wish all the cocoons in this tree picked." She smiled when she saw the horrified expression on his face. A player of the samisen climbing a tree!

The dancing girls shook with laughter. This was fun. It was good to see their mistress pink with excitement, homesickness forgotten. Quite willingly they spent the afternoon unwinding cocoons, first soaking them in hot tea. Then they twisted strands together to make threads. After that the maids wound the threads onto a smooth branch.

The Empress now called in the court carpenters. "I wish a special loom built before day-break tomorrow," she told them. "A loom that will take a thread finer than any cotton or wool. On it I shall weave a new kind of cloth. A royal cloth, pale as the sun on a winter morning. But mind you, not a word to anyone! It is my secret."

The carpenters looked at one another. What had come over the little Empress? Had she lost her mind because of sadness? Why would she make cloth with her own hands? There were plenty of servants to do all the weaving. But the carpenters did make the loom. Foolish or not, it was wise to obey the slightest wish of the Emperor's young bride.

Si-Ling-Shi scarcely slept that night. It was such fun to have a plan, especially a secret plan.

Surely the Emperor would be pleased with such a robe as she dreamed for him. That is, if her idea worked.

Next morning she was up with the sun. The carpenters brought the new loom. Working in her own room where curious eyes could not peer, Si-Ling-Shi began threading warp and woof with the shining thread.

When she did not appear, all the court began to whisper. "Is the Empress weeping alone in her room?" asked one of the courtiers. "Can no one think of a way to amuse her?" another one said.

The Emperor's ministers were pale with worry. They, too, had lain awake all night, though for a different reason. What would become of them they dared not think. For neither one of them had found a way to keep their mistress' thoughts from the home of her childhood.

At last it was high noon. The ministers, worried and frightened, came to the Emperor.

"Well!" he declared sternly. "What do you suggest as a way of making the Empress happy?"

The first minister spoke in an uncertain voice. "Perhaps a pet peacock might delight Her

Highness, with the splendid colors of its tail," he said.

"Humph!" was the Emperor's scornful reply.

"Or a pool where she might swim," said the other hastily.

The Emperor overlooked the unhappy men entirely. "Send for Her Highness!" he ordered.

Someone whispered in his ear, and then the Emperor was very angry. "Alone in her room?" he cried. "Why has no one told me this before?" He leaped from the throne and rushed to comfort his unhappy bride.

But the Empress he found was far from unhappy. Si-Ling-Shi sat in front of her loom, tossing the shuttle back and forth, in an easy rhythm. And from the loom there came a length of shining cloth such as no one had ever seen before.

"What are you doing, my love?" the Emperor asked, looking for signs of tears on her pink cheeks.

Si-Ling-Shi looked up at him happily. "Making a present for you, my lord," she said. "A new kind of cloth for a royal robe. Isn't it beautiful?"

So Si-Ling-Shi told him about the cocoon that had fallen into her tea. "You are not angry with me?" she asked timidly.

"Angry?" the Emperor asked. "Who could be angry about so rare a gift? Or at finding a bride happy instead of sad? I would give half of my kingdom never to see another tear on your cheeks."

"Then may I ask a gift from *you*, my lord?" Si-Ling-Shi asked boldly. "I should like a grove of a thousand mulberry trees. Then I will have many worms to spin cocoons for me. And endless miles of thread for weaving this cloth."

And so it was that silk was discovered. To this day the Chinese people call this precious cloth "Si" in honor of the little Empress. As for Si-Ling-Shi, her homesickness disappeared like a cloud before the sun of happiness. In addition to silk, she had discovered still another secret—that busy hands are happy hands, and that loving hearts are joyful.

The Emperor touched the cloth and saw that it gleamed with wondrous beauty. It was indeed fit for an Emperor.

"What have you done, my dove?" he asked in amazement. "Where did you find such a beautiful thread?"

She lived for many years, tending her silkworms in her thousand mulberry trees. She learned to dye silk thread with beautiful colors. Si-Ling-Shi is known now as "Goddess of the Silkworms." Later Empresses of China set aside one day each year to feed silkworms in her honor.

For two thousand years the Chinese kept Si-Ling-Shi's secret for their own. In all the world they were the only people who knew where silk came from. They were the only people who knew that silk was discovered by a homesick Empress, when one small cocoon fell into her teacup.

On Your Own

1. Why was the little Empress homesick and unhappy? How did the Emperor try to make her happy? Why did the things he tried fail to make her happy? What two secrets did she discover?

2. What was done to honor the little Empress for her discovery of silk?

3. Look up *silk* in an encyclopedia. Why does the silkworm spin the fine thread that goes into silk cloth?

4. The words below were used in the story to describe the making of cloth. Use the glossary or a dictionary to find the meaning of each.

    (a) fiber   (c) woof   (e) loom
    (b) warp   (d) shuttle   (f) weave

TWO FABLES

Retold by NORAH MONTGOMERIE

Watch for the wisdom that is passed on to you in these fables.

The Travelers and the Bear

Two friends were traveling along a road together when they saw a Bear coming towards them. One of them was so frightened he immediately climbed up a tree, leaving his friend to face the Bear.

The other, realizing he was helpless, threw himself on the ground and pretended to be dead, for he had heard that a bear will not touch a dead body.

When the Bear came up to the man, he stood over him

sniffing at his nose and ears. But the traveler held his breath and kept perfectly still, although he was terrified. At last the Bear, thinking he was dead, walked away without harming him at all.

When the traveler was quite sure that the Bear was well out of sight, he picked himself up off the ground. Only then did his friend climb down the tree, saying:

"That was a narrow escape."

"It was indeed," said the traveler to his friend.

"I saw the Bear whisper in your ear. What did he say?" asked the friend.

"He said it is wiser to travel alone than with a companion who is a coward. I think he was right and that is what I mean to do."

And away he went on the road alone.

The Date Gatherers

A King once asked his servants to fill seven large baskets with dates from his palm trees. The servants took the baskets, climbed the trees, picked the dates, and threw them into the baskets. This was quite hard work, but when they came to a tree that had fallen they found they could gather the fruit from it in no time.

"What a pity it is that all the trees aren't lying on the ground," said one of them. "It would make our task so much easier."

"Let us cut them down then," said another.

So they cut down the rest of the trees, and soon the seven large baskets were filled with fruit. They laughed and felt very pleased with themselves, for they thought they had done the work quickly and well.

"We'd better replant the trees before we return to the palace," they said.

143

They tried to plant the trees again, but somehow they would not remain upright, and the leaves were already limp.

"They'll be all right in the morning," said the servants as they lifted the baskets onto their heads.

"Well done," said the King, as the baskets were set down before him. "You've done well, and quickly too. You shall have your reward in the morning."

But next morning, when the King looked out from his balcony, he saw all his palm trees lying withered on the ground.

"What has happened to my trees?" he shouted.

When he heard what had indeed happened he was more angry than ever, and instead of being rewarded for their work, the servants were punished for their stupidity.

On Your Own

1. A fable is a short story that teaches a lesson. Match each of these lessons with its fable.
   (a) Haste makes waste.
   (b) It is wiser to go alone than with a coward.

2. Which characters in the fables do you think were wise? List them. Which characters do you think were foolish? List them. Be ready to give reasons for your answers.

The Tinder Box

By Hans Christian Andersen

It was just a little box. But it was a magic box for
those who knew how to use it.

The Soldier and the Old Witch

A soldier came marching
along the highroad. One, two!
One, two! He had his knapsack
on his back and his sword at his
side, for he had been to the wars
and now he was on his way
home. He met an old witch on
the road. She was so ugly that
her lower lip hung right down
onto her chin.

She said, "Good evening, soldier! What a nice sword you've got, and such a big knapsack. You are a real soldier! You shall have as much money as ever you like."

"Thank you kindly, you old witch," said the soldier.

"Do you see that big tree?" said the witch, pointing to a tree close by. "It is hollow inside.

Climb up to the top and you will see a hole into which you can let yourself down, right down under the tree. I will tie a rope around your waist so that I can haul you up again when you call."

"What am I to do down under the tree?" asked the soldier.

"Fetch money," said the witch. "You must know that when you get down to the bottom of the tree you will find yourself in a wide passage. It's quite light there, for there are over a hundred blazing lamps. You will see three doors which you can open, for the keys are there.

"If you go into the first room you will see a big box in the middle of the floor. A dog is sitting on the top of it and he has eyes as big as saucers, but you needn't mind that. I will give you my blue-checked apron, which you can spread out on the floor. Go quickly forward, take up the dog, and put him on my apron. Then open the box and take out as much money as you like. It is all copper."

"Copper?" asked the soldier.

"Yes, copper," said the witch. "But if you like silver better, go into the second room. In this room you will find a dog with eyes as big as millstones. But never mind that. Put him on my apron and take the money."

"Silver?" asked the soldier.

"Yes, silver," said the witch. "But if you like gold better, go into the third room. You can have gold, and as much as you can carry. But the dog sitting on that box has eyes each as big as the Round Tower. He *is* a dog, indeed, as you may imagine. But don't let it trouble you. You only have to put him on my apron. Then he won't hurt you, and you can take as much gold out of the box as ever you like!"

"That's not so bad," said the soldier. "But what am I to give you, old witch? You'll want something, I'll be bound."

"No," said the witch. "Not a single penny do I want. I only want you to bring me an old tinder box that my grandmother forgot the last time she was down at the bottom of the tree."

"Well, tie the rope round my waist then," said the soldier.

"Here it is," said the witch. "And here is my blue-checked apron."

Then the soldier climbed up the tree. He let himself slide down the hollow trunk, and found himself, as the witch had said, in the wide passage. Here the many hundred lamps were burning.

Now he opened the first door. Ugh! There sat the dog with eyes as big as saucers staring at him.

"You are a nice fellow!" said the soldier as he put him onto the witch's apron. He took out as many pennies as he could stuff into his pockets. Then he shut the box, put the dog on the top of it again, and went into

the next room. Hello! There sat the dog with eyes as big as millstones.

"You shouldn't stare at me so hard. You might get a pain in your eyes!" said the soldier. Then he put the dog on the apron. But when he saw all the silver in the box, he threw away all the coppers and stuffed his pockets and his knapsack with silver.

Then the soldier went into the third room. Oh, how terrible! That dog really had two eyes as big as the Round Tower, and they rolled around like wheels.

"Good evening," said the soldier, saluting, for he had never seen such a dog in his life. After looking at him for a bit, he lifted him down onto the apron and opened the chest. Heavens! What a lot of gold! He could buy the whole of Copenhagen with it, and all the sugar pigs from the cake woman. He could buy all the tin soldiers, whips, and rocking horses in the world. That was money indeed! Now the soldier threw away all the silver and filled his pockets and his knapsack with gold. Yes, he stuffed all his pockets, his knapsack, his hat, and his boots so full that he could hardly walk. Now, he really had a lot of money. He put the dog back on the box, shut the door, and shouted up through the tree, "Haul me up, you old witch!"

"Have you the tinder box?"

"Oh, to be sure!" said the soldier. "I had quite forgotten it."

And he went back to fetch it. The witch hauled him up. There he was standing on the highroad again with his pockets, boots, knapsack, and hat full of gold.

"What do you want the tinder box for?" asked the soldier.

"That's no business of yours," said the witch. "You have the money. Now give me the tinder box!"

"Stuff and nonsense!" said the soldier. "Tell me directly what you want with it or I will draw my sword on you!"

"I won't!" said the witch.

Then the soldier drew his sword. Away the witch ran down the highroad. The soldier tied all the money up in her apron and flung it on his back like a pack. Then he put the tinder box in his pocket, and marched off to town.

The Soldier in the Town

It was a beautiful town. The soldier went straight to the finest house and bought it. He had the grandest rooms and all

the food he liked best, because he was a rich man now that he had so much money.

Certainly the servant who had to clean his boots thought they were funny old things for such a rich gentleman. The soldier had not had time yet to buy any new ones, but the next day he bought new boots and fine clothes. The soldier now became a fine gentleman. The people told him all about the grand things in the town, and about their King, and what a lovely princess his daughter was.

"Where is she to be seen?" asked the soldier.

"You can't see her at all," they said. "She lives in a great copper castle surrounded by walls and towers. Nobody but the King dares to go in and out, for it has been foretold that she will marry a soldier. The King doesn't like that!"

"I should like to see her well enough," thought the soldier. But there was no way of getting permission for that.

He now led a very merry life. He went to plays, drove about in the King's Park, and gave away a lot of money to poor people. He remembered how disagreeable it used to be not to have a penny in his pocket. Now he was rich, wore fine clothes, and had a great many friends who all said what a nice fellow he was. They said he was a perfect gentleman, and he liked to be told that.

But as he went on spending money every day, he at last found himself with only two pennies left. Then he was obliged to move out of his fine house. He had to live in a tiny little attic up under the roof, clean his own boots, and mend them himself. None of his friends went to see him because there were far too many stairs.

One dark evening when he had not even enough money to buy a candle with, he suddenly remembered the tinder box. There was a little bit of candle in it. He got out the tinder box and struck fire. The sparks flew out from the flint. Then the door burst open, and the dog with eyes as big as saucers stood before him and said,

"What does my lord command?"

"By heaven!" said the soldier, "this is a nice kind of tinder box. I can get whatever I want with this. Get me some money," he said to the dog, and away it went.

The dog was back in a twinkling with a bag full of pennies in its mouth. Now the soldier saw what a treasure he had in the tinder box. If he struck once, the dog which sat on the box of copper came. And if he struck twice, the dog on the silver box came. And if he struck three times, the one from the box of gold came.

He now moved back to the grand house and got his fine clothes again. Then all his friends knew him once more and liked him as much as ever.

The Soldier and the Princess

One night the soldier suddenly began to think, "After all, it's a curious thing that no man can get a sight of the Princess. Everyone says she is so beautiful! But what is the good of that when she always has to be shut up in that big copper palace with all the towers? Can I not somehow manage to see her? Where is my tinder box?" Then he struck the flint and, whisk! There came the dog with eyes as big as saucers.

The soldier said, "I am very anxious to see the Princess, if only for a moment."

The dog was out of the door in an instant. Before the soldier had time to think about it, the dog was back again with the Princess. There she was, fast asleep on the dog's back. She was so lovely that anybody could see that she must be a real princess. The soldier could not help it; he was obliged to kiss her, for he was a true soldier.

Then the dog ran back to the palace with the Princess. In the morning, when the King and Queen were having breakfast, the Princess said that she had such a wonderful dream about a dog and a soldier. She had ridden on the dog's back and the soldier had kissed her.

"That's a pretty tale," said the Queen.

After this an old lady-in-waiting had to sit by the Princess' bed at night to see if this was really a dream.

The soldier longed to see the Princess again, if only for a moment. That night he sent the dog to fetch her.

The dog took up the Princess and ran off with her as fast as he could. But the old lady-in-waiting put on her overshoes and ran just as fast behind them. When she saw that they disappeared into the soldier's house, she thought, "Now I know where it is," and made a mark with chalk on the door. Then she went home and told the King and Queen about it.

Presently the dog came out with the Princess. When he saw that there was a mark on the door, he took a bit of chalk, too, and made marks on all the doors in the town.

Early next morning the King, the Queen, the lady-in-waiting, and all the court officials went to look for the soldier's house. "There it is," said the King, when he saw the first door with a mark on it.

"No, my dear husband, it is there," said the Queen, who saw another door with a mark on it.

"But there is one! And there is another!" they all cried out.

They soon saw that it was hopeless to try to find the right house.

Now the Queen was a very clever woman. She knew more than how to ride in a coach. She took her big scissors and cut up a large piece of silk into small pieces and made a pretty little bag which she filled with fine grains of buckwheat. She then tied it onto the back of the

Princess. And when that was done, she cut a little hole in the bag, so that the grains could drop out and show where the Princess went.

That night the dog came again. He took the Princess on his back, and ran off with her as fast as he could. He never noticed how the buckwheat grains dropped out all along the road from the palace to the soldier's house.

In the morning the King and the Queen easily saw where their daughter had been, and they seized the soldier and threw him into prison.

There he lay. Oh, how dark and tiresome it was! And then one day he was told, "Tomorrow you are to be hanged." It was not amusing to be told that, especially as he had left his tinder box behind him at his house.

In the morning he heard the drums and the soldiers marching along. He looked through the bars of the little window. He saw the people hurrying out of town to see him hanged.

Among them was a shoemaker's boy in his leather apron and slippers. He was in such a hurry that he lost one of his slippers and it fell close under the soldier's window.

"I say, boy! Don't be in such a hurry," said the soldier. "Nothing will happen till I get there. But if you will run to the house where I used to live and fetch me my tinder box, you shall have a penny. You must put your best foot foremost." The boy was only too glad to have the penny, and he tore off to get the tinder box. He gave it to the soldier.

Outside the town a high platform had been raised. The soldiers and the people were drawn up around it. The King and the Queen sat upon a beautiful throne exactly opposite the judge and all the court officials.

The soldier mounted the ladder to the platform. When the men were about to put the rope around his neck, he asked the King to grant him one last wish. He wanted very much to smoke a pipe as it would be his last pipe in this world. The King granted him his wish. The soldier took out his tinder box and struck fire, once, twice, three times. And there were all the dogs—the one with eyes like saucers, the one with eyes like millstones, and the one with eyes as big as the Round Tower.

"Help me! Save me from being hanged," cried the soldier.

And then the dogs rushed at the soldiers and the officials. The dogs took them one by one and threw them up high into the air.

"Call off your dogs!" cried the King.

"I won't," said the soldier. "I won't, unless I may marry the Princess."

"Yes, yes!" said the King. "You may have the Princess for your bride."

All the people shouted, "Oh, good soldier, you shall be our Prince and live in the palace!"

Then they conducted the soldier to the King's coach. The Princess came out of the copper palace and joined him. They rode with the King and Queen, and the court officials rode behind. All three dogs danced along in front of them and shouted "Hurrah!" The boys all put their fingers in their mouths and whistled, and the soldiers presented arms.

The wedding took place in a week, and the dogs all had seats at the table, where they sat staring with all their eyes.

On Your Own

1. Look up *tinder box* in the glossary. What was the tinder box? How did the soldier happen to learn its magic? What did he gain from it?

2. Find in the story the more interesting ways of saying these things.
   (a) The witch was very ugly.
   (b) The dogs had big eyes.
   (c) He could buy many things with the money.
   (d) The Queen knew a great deal.

3. If you had a magic box, what would you wish for? Use your imagination and write a story about a magic box.

COULD IT HAVE BEEN A SHADOW?

By MONICA SHANNON

What ran under the rosebush?
    What ran under the stone?
Could it have been a shadow,
    Running away alone?
Maybe a fairy's shadow,
    Slipping away at dawn
To guard a gleaming pot of gold
    For a busy leprechaun.

FLINT

By CHRISTINA ROSSETTI

An emerald is as green as grass;
    A ruby red as blood;
A sapphire shines as blue as heaven;
    A flint lies in the mud.

A diamond is a brilliant stone,
    To catch the world's desire;
An opal holds a fiery spark;
    But a flint holds fire.

Thinking It Through

1. Each of the following things was important in one of the stories. Which story was each one in and why was it important?

   (a) box   (d) tea   (g) axe

   (b) dates   (e) bear   (h) wheelbarrow

   (c) crab   (f) fox

2. Pretend that you are one of the characters. How do you think you would have felt if you had been:

   (a) The little Empress when she saw the cocoon unwinding in her teacup?

   (b) Peter when the old man gave him the wheelbarrow?

   (c) The woodcutter when the man who made only noises claimed the money?

   (d) The soldier when the huge-eyed dogs first appeared?

   Think of other things that happened and be ready to act out the part of one of the characters.

3. Which of these old tales do you like best? Why? Bring in one or more books of old tales and help to set up a display in the classroom. You may wish to read aloud or tell one of your favorite old tales.

4. Help to plan and give the play, "Dr. Know-All," or a play made from another old tale chosen by the class.

Jack-O'-Lantern

By RUTH H. COLBY

You will be surprised to find out how Jonathan, a
Puritan boy of New England, celebrated Halloween.

"Mother, can't I even light a candle in it?" Jonathan Wheeler spoke pleadingly.

"You know your father doesn't like such things."

"I know, Mother. They were wrong when he was little. But even Parson Smith said we might frolic this Halloween. Father's—" he hesitated and then brought it out firmly, "Father's old-fashioned."

"You mustn't speak in such a way, Jonathan," his mother said.

"But it's such a beauty, Mother!" said Jonathan's sister, Prudence. "It has a mouth full of teeth and great big eyes."

"Prudence," her mother's voice was gentle, "Father doesn't hold with these new-fangled ideas. He thinks that Halloween is a heathen festival, as indeed it was once. He

doesn't want any jack-o'-lanterns in this house."

"So I can't even light a candle in it." Jonathan's mouth turned down at the corners.

He himself had picked the huge yellow pumpkin from the south meadow, had scooped it out, and carefully cut the big eyes and nose and grinning, tooth-filled mouth. Leslie Faxton, the boy who had just come from England, had shown him how. He had hardly been able to wait for Halloween to light up the huge face. And now he would never know how that mouth would look with a flame back of it.

In the little Puritan town of Quambog, Halloween had never been celebrated. Many of the older people still objected to its merriment. Some even thought that Parson Smith was much too young and much too newfangled in his ways.

Mrs. Wheeler saw the downturned mouth.

"Father and I are going to Stonington in the carriage," she said. "They say a ship is there and that in it there is a shipment of oranges. Perhaps I can get you one apiece."

"What are oranges, Mother?"

"Fruit, dear, yellow, and most healthful, they say."

"Like pumpkins, Mother?"

"No, dear, not at all. Wait till you see one. I shall be back before dark. But, Prudence, you might set the table and heat the cornmeal mush. Perhaps you might scrape a little maple sugar. The blue sugar bowl is almost empty."

Two little faces still looked downcast.

"You might decorate the table," she went on. "Jonathan always finds lovely things outdoors and Father likes them so. And, Prue, you might put on your new dress. You can pretend you're receiving company, Father and me."

Jonathan's face brightened, and Prudence smiled. She loved the new red dress, dyed with dye made from dark red sumac blooms.

The sunny afternoon went by quickly. Jonathan helped Prudence scrape the maple sugar cakes into soft tan flakes. They filled the blue sugar bowl to the top.

Then both went out into the sunlight, down past Darkhollow Brook, dim and gloomy like its name, to the south pasture.

Here Jonathan found a pumpkin. "As long as the pumpkin hasn't a face on him, Father won't mind him on the table, Prue."

Prue laughed. "We'll put him on the big pewter plate in

the center. We'll polish some apples and put them around him."

"I'll get some of those brown oak leaves," said Jonathan, "just over the wall."

"Look, Jon, how pretty!" Prudence answered, for the wall was covered with the blossoms of clematis, gone to seed, soft and downy as the loveliest fairy wool. "If we pick the vines carefully we can trail it over the leaves and fruit. It will be a lovely table."

Jon nodded soberly. He was still remembering his handsome jack-o'-lantern. He did so long to see its face all fiery.

It was beginning to get dark, as the children crossed Darkhollow Brook on stepping stones. They had to balance themselves carefully, for their hands were full.

Beyond the brook they reached the path leading to the house. The big ball of the sun was setting fast, and every little window in the house was glittering yellow. Jon thought it looked like a pumpkin itself, round and yellow.

Prue was looking at Darkhollow Brook. Suddenly she clutched Jon's arm. "Something's moving down there in Darkhollow."

Both children strained their eyes. Jon dropped his pumpkin, as he caught sight of two dark shapes stealing through the shadows.

"Prue, it's Indian Jim! Probably his brother Joe is with him!"

"Oh, let's get in quick!" Prue fairly flew across the meadow, Jon right behind her.

There were few Indians left in Quambog, and those few were quiet, peaceable folk. Indian Jim was the one bad character. He was likely to steal whatever he could lay his hands on. He and his brother Joe were sometimes ugly in their speech.

"Quick, bar the door, Jon!" said Prue.

Jon needed no hurrying. The heavy bar, rarely used, was

pushed into place, and Prudence felt a little comforted. It looked so strong. The old house had stood off Indian attacks before.

"The shutters, Jon!"

The two children closed the heavy wooden shutters. The room was quite dark now except for firelight.

From force of habit Prue set the cornmeal mush near the open fire to warm. She wondered who would eat it. If only Father and Mother would come! But there were no welcome sounds of hooves or wheels. Instead the silence seemed to grow heavier. It was getting almost too dark to see each other.

"It's a funny Halloween, Prue." Jon managed a grin.

"Remember how Leslie Faxton told us about witches and how they scared——" Jon seized Prue. "I've got it, Prue! Get a candle! Quick!"

He raced down to the cellar. Prudence felt her heart beat faster when she was left alone in the room. But she found a candle.

Jon puffed up the cellar stairs. In his arms, held tightly, was the big jack-o'-lantern.

"Quick, Prue, the north room where there's no firelight. We can see the Indians leave Dark-hollow if we watch. Hold your candle so they can't see it."

They tiptoed into the north room. It was very dark. Jon set the big jack-o'-lantern on the floor. Then he took the candle and fastened it inside the pumpkin. The great grinning face fairly leaped out at them in the darkness. Both children gazed at it, astonished, and just a little horrified, for this was the first jack-o'-lantern they had ever seen. It was a fiery goblin, as Leslie Faxton had said. And Father didn't believe in it.

Jon knelt by the window. "Watch closely. We can see anyone against the sky. Most likely, Jim and his brother will go to the barn first, to see what they can take."

"Oh, would they take my Daisy calf?" said Prue.

"She's a good calf," Jon said. He sounded so much like Father that ordinarily Prue would have smiled. Now she was too worried.

Jon clutched her arm. "Isn't that something moving, Prue? There, just leaving the bushes!"

They could just make out two figures close together. The Indians were stealing toward the big barn. That brought them face to face with the front of the house.

Jon, his jaw set firmly, lifted the lighted jack-o'-lantern and set it on the windowsill, its fiery face outward . . .

Mr. and Mrs. Wheeler, Jon's and Prue's father and mother, were glad to be so near home.

"The house is all dark, Father," said Mrs. Wheeler. "How queer!"

Before her husband could answer, a grinning, glowing face appeared out of the darkness. Mrs. Wheeler gasped. It *did* look like a fiery monster suspended in the air, grinning.

Mr. Wheeler shut his lips tightly. Jonathan should . . .

Two horrifying, high-pitched yells cut through the still night air. There was a sound of swift, running feet. Two dark shapes bounded by the carriage, as the frightened horses dashed up the lane. Mr. Wheeler had all he could do to hold the horses.

165

Mrs. Wheeler, white-faced, flung herself at the door. She heard a heavy bar pushed back. There on the doorsill was Prue, sobbing, and Jon, his jaw still shut tight, trembling a little. They threw themselves into her arms.

It was the merriest supper the Wheelers ever had.

Prudence's dark red dress glowed like the sumac blooms in the fall. Over the fireplace were brown oak leaves and the trailing fairy wool of clematis vines. On the shelf were red apples polished like red glass. Between them was a strange new fruit, orange balls about the same size. Jon and Prue thought them beautiful.

But in the center of the table, in the place of honor, on Grandmother's pewter plate, was a fiery-faced jack-o'-lantern with a great wide smile.

Mr. Wheeler's smile was almost as wide.

On Your Own

1. Why did Mr. Wheeler object to the children's having a jack-o'-lantern? Was he right in thinking that Halloween was once a heathen festival? Use an encyclopedia to find out how Halloween began.

2. Why was Mr. Wheeler angry when he saw the jack-o'-lantern? Why was he glad later? Do you think Jon was disobedient when he used the jack-o'-lantern? Give your reasons.

3. Have you ever had an experience when you had to be bold enough to use your own judgment and protect yourself or others? Compare your experience with Jon's.

Prairie Fire

By ELIZABETH COATSWORTH

Ilse and her family came across the country from
Boston to Kansas in a covered wagon. They lived on
the prairie in the wagon while Papa built the sod house.
Later came the fire—and danger and bravery.

One hot afternoon when the
wind was blowing from the
south, Ilse was puzzled to see
that a black cloud was coming
up over the curving horizon of
the prairie.

"There's going to be rain,"
she called to Papa and Mama,

who were inside the house. Papa came to the door to look.

The cloud was very black and it was moving fast. Already it was towering above the prairie, and the sunlit grass and flowers seemed very bright against it.

A rabbit came bounding past the house, never glancing at them. Another followed. Then a flock of birds flew by, sounding cries of alarm.

The black cloud was whirling upwards as it approached. Mama came to the door.

"I smell smoke, Friedrich!" she cried.

"You are right, Maria! The prairie's on fire!" Papa said. "Close the doors and windows while I get Little Peter! We'll be safe by the river."

That day Little Peter, their gray horse, was picketed to one side of the house by himself. Papa ran and brought him back, snorting and fidgeting. It was hard to keep him still long enough to get Mama on his back. When Papa lifted Hans into her arms, Little Peter jumped and Hans hit his head against Mama's shoulder and began to cry. Papa swung Ilse up behind Mama.

"Hold tight, Ilse," he said, and they were off, Papa running by Little Peter's side, holding the halter. The horse kept throwing up his head, trying to free himself from Papa's hand. He snorted and plunged so that Papa had all he could do not to be thrown off his feet and trampled. Hans was frightened and his head hurt. He bawled and struggled in Mama's arms. It was hard for her to hold him.

And just then Ilse, looking backwards, saw Baldy, the cow. Baldy was trying to pull her picket chain loose, but she could not budge it. She was mooing and her eyes rolled. Ilse could not leave her there. Papa had always said that she must take good care of Baldy.

"I'm getting Baldy," she called to Mama, as she slipped from Little Peter's back. But Mama, trying to quiet the struggling Hans and to keep her seat at the same time, never heard her, nor felt her hands loosen from her waist. Papa did not see her, either.

Alone across the prairie Ilse ran. The black cloud towered above her like one of the wicked genii. Now below it she could see the red of running flames, and the howling of the wind was mixed with the cries of birds flying before it. A big rabbit struck against her legs and nearly knocked her over, but she ran on.

By the time she had unfastened Baldy, it was too late to reach the river. They were cut off by a wall of fire. The sun was darkened and ashes were blowing about them. But Ilse did not lose her head. She

169

must get Baldy into the sod barn at least, and Baldy, too, was glad to seek shelter in the stall that had always meant safety to her.

Panting in the darkness of the windowless building, Ilse looked about. Only the door would burn. If she could wet it down, now! The spring was not far off.

She jerked a horse blanket from the hook on which it hung. There were no pails in the barn as the animals were taken to the spring to drink, but a wet blanket would not burn easily. Closing the door behind her to keep Baldy in, Ilse ran stumbling towards the spring. All about her tongues of flames, torn loose by the wind from the roaring fire which followed, were flying by her. The air was hard to breathe.

She reached the spring and wet the blanket. But now it weighed so much that she could scarcely drag it after her. Still, she did not give up easily. She was stumbling over the sod now, and the dry grass was catching fire here and there about her. The great wall of flame was rushing down upon her. Already it was spreading about and encircling the barn as a fiery river might spread about and encircle a huge rock. The sod house, too, was surrounded by fire. She was lost.

But even now, Ilse kept her head. The heavy wet blanket dragged at her arms, as though reminding her that it was there. It was her only hope. Spreading it out on the plowed sod, she crawled under it, making herself as small as she could. Her chest pressed against the ground, and she felt something hard and small against it.

"Are you all right Thumbelina?" she whispered to her little doll. She thought she heard Thumbelina whisper back, "I'm all right."

Then the roaring filled her ears, and a great something crawled over her across the wet blanket, making a sizzling sound, and in a moment had

passed by. She heard the up-
roar of the fire racing on and on
across the prairie, driven by the
wind. Further and further off
it sounded, and at last she dared
lift up the steaming blanket.
She was not hurt. All about her
the ground lay black, with here
and there a wisp of smoke curling up from it, or a feeble
tongue of fire dying as she
watched it. The grass and
flowers were burned from the
sod roofs of the house and barn,
but the buildings were standing.
Even the smoke-blackened windows in the house were not
broken, but the doors were
smoldering.

Now she could walk across
the ashes. When Papa and
Mama hurried back they found
Ilse hard at work with the milk-
ing pail, throwing water against
the house door. She had already put out the fire eating at
the barn door. She looked
black as a chimney sweep.

"Baldy's safe," she called to
them. "And Thumbelina's all
right, too!"

Papa and Mama did not scold Ilse for the fright she had given them when at the river they found that she was not with them. They listened to her story and knew how well she had done her duty.

"A miss is as good as a mile," said Papa. "The fire never came down into the river bottom at all. Thanks to you and the fact that the doors are made of green wood and didn't catch fire easily, no harm has been done, except to the garden, and we can plant that again!"

On Your Own

1. Was Ilse disobedient or not when she went back to take care of Baldy? Why do you think so? What was her plan? Why didn't it work out? Do you think Ilse realized the danger she would have to face when she decided to return? Give your reasons.

2. What did Ilse do to save the cow? The barn? Herself? Why was it a help that the house and barn were made of sod? Why was it that Ilse's parents did not scold her?

3. Choose from this list words that describe Ilse. Prove your points by reading from the story.

proud	brave	kind	steady
unselfish	lazy	helpless	wicked

4. Make a picture of the prairie fire.

Vanilla Village

By PRISCILLA CARDEN

Chombo, a Mexican Indian boy, had an exciting
adventure with bandits.

Chombo's Journey

It was sunset. High in the
mountains, deep in the forest, a
little Indian village shone white
under the flaming sky. All the
houses were quiet, all but one.
All the merry children would
soon be asleep, all but one.

Chombo's house was wide
awake. It twinkled with yellow
candlelight. It hummed with

voices. Out in the yard, strong little burros stood waiting.

And on the back of a burro sat Chombo himself, all alone. He sat very straight, his arms folded, his brown eyes sparkling. An exciting journey was about to begin, and Chombo didn't mean to be left behind.

Proudly, he looked at the great baskets that stood ready along the wall. Each basket was heaped high with sweet-smelling vanilla beans, dark and ripe.

Chombo was an Indian boy. He lived in Mexico, in a little village high above the sea. The village was a Vanilla Village. All the Indian families raised vanilla. Now it was harvest time, and in every yard the vanilla beans were spread out to ripen, or gathered into baskets. The whole village smelled sweetly of vanilla, and when the wind blew, the fragrance traveled far, far out into the great green forest.

When the vanilla was ripe, the Indians carried it down the long road to the sea, and there it was sold.

Sometimes the vanilla didn't reach the sea. Sometimes bandits hid along the road, and held up the Indians, and stole the vanilla. This year family after family had been held up.

That is why Chombo's big brothers had decided to travel by night with their load of vanilla. And tonight they would start. Chombo waited, tingling with excitement.

A pair of tall Indian boys came quietly out of the house. They were his brothers, Luis and Marcos. They looked at the sky.

Behind the mountains in the West the red sun had gone down. Behind the mountains in the East the silvery moon was floating up.

"Time to start," said Luis softly. "Now let's load up the burros!"

Without noticing Chombo, they crossed the dim yard. Each boy picked up a great vanilla basket.

"This way, this way," sang out Chombo. "Load up this burro first!"

His two tall brothers halted in surprise.

"Well, well!" said Luis. "Where are you going, young one?"

"With you, with you," pleaded Chombo. "Please, please, let me come!"

"And what if we get held up by the bandits?"

"Then I'll help you fight," cried Chombo.

"You're too young to be a help!"

Marcos said, "Oh, let him come! After all, we're sure to get through safely! Everybody else has traveled in broad daylight."

Good-naturedly, Luis gave in. "Well, all right! Chombo can come!"

Somewhere in the forest, the vanilla bandits had a secret place. No one knew where it was. The police had hunted and hunted, but no one could find it.

Little Mariquita, Chombo's younger sister, came out of the house. She was a sturdy little girl with black braids, and she wore a short white dress. She marched straight to Chombo.

"Lift me up!" she said. "I want to go with you!"

But Luis said, "No, Chombo, she can't go!"

"But I *will*," said Mariquita. Sometimes she could be stubborn.

Mother took Mariquita's hand. "You're too little," she said. "And besides, baby and

I need you here at home. Who would help me, if you went away?"

Chombo forgot about Mariquita as he watched his brothers hang the guns on their backs. The baby began to cry just then, so Mother went into the house. Father came out. He and Luis and Marcos finished the loading. Soon each little burro was carrying two great baskets of vanilla beans. Now the journey was going to begin.

Mother came out. "Where is Mariquita?" she asked.

Everybody looked. Nobody saw Mariquita.

"Never mind," said Father. "You must be off! We'll find Mariquita after you leave. Good-by!"

Everybody waved, as Luis and Marcos led the burros out at the gate and down the road.

The forest closed over their heads. Only a little moonlight shone through, crisscrossing the trail with silver.

"We're in bandit country now!" thought Chombo.

On and on jogged the burros. A sweet smell stole from the vanilla baskets. It crept into the mysterious forest, and the night wind carried it on and on.

Luis and Marcos held their guns ready.

Chombo's head would nod, his eyes would close. Presently he knew that his burro had stopped, and that his brothers were standing beside him. He heard Luis say softly, "Just look at him! He'll be tumbling off the burro."

And Marcos answered, "Let's put him in a vanilla basket, and let him sleep."

They lifted Chombo off the burro. They tucked him into a great roomy vanilla basket, on top of the fragrant beans.

Escape from the Bandits

Something happened a little later, but Chombo knew nothing about it. He didn't see the dark figures leaping silently from the forest. He didn't see his brothers struggling bravely, trying to warn him. In an instant they were borne down, gagged and tied. He didn't know when they were left behind, lying helplessly by the trail.

The boy in the vanilla basket slept on. But little by little he began to wake up. Something seemed wrong to him.

Jog, jog! On plodded the burros.

A whip cracked. He listened drowsily. Crack! Crack! But Luis and Marcos didn't have any whip.

"Faster!" growled someone. Who?

All at once, Chombo was wide awake. Very watchfully, he peeped over the edge of the basket. Strange men were all around, strange men riding on horses. They were driving the burros onward into the moonlit forest.

Vanilla bandits had captured the burros! They were stealing the vanilla. They were stealing Chombo, too! What had they done with his brothers?

The bandit chief, mounted on a handsome brown pony, was riding close beside him. Chombo dug down again into the vanilla beans. Down, down he went. The friendly beans closed over his head so that the bandits could not see him. Presently he slept.

Thump! Down on a stone floor went Chombo's vanilla basket. Immediately the boy was awake. He heard a waterfall, very loud and very close. The air was damp. Where was he?

Hooves clattered on stone. Voices growled. And then there were sighings and gruntings, as the bandits lay down to sleep.

"Now this is my chance!" thought Chombo. "But first I must let them go to sleep, every last one!"

Indian children know how to wait. The minutes passed, and still Chombo didn't move. At last, without a sound, he peeped out at the bandits.

What a sight he saw! Now he knew why the police never had found the hideaway of the vanilla bandits. It was a cave, a very narrow cave behind a waterfall!

The horses and burros dozed along the left wall, and along the right the bandits were lying fast asleep, rolled in blankets. Straight ahead hung the misty waterfall.

Strangest of all, there didn't seem to be a way out!

But Chombo wasn't scared, not yet. Thrilled and wondering, he climbed out of the basket. The bandit chief's brown pony turned its head and watched him. The little boy and the pony looked quietly at each other.

Tiptoeing all around the cave, he looked carefully for the secret way out. But the cave walls were solid rock, without a crack, without a trace of a door. And across the entrance hung the misty waterfall. Chombo returned to his basket no wiser than when he had set out.

And now, for the first time, he felt frightened. He was trapped, trapped in the cave with the bandits! He wanted to cry. He wanted to shout for help. But he only stood quite still, blinking back the tears and looking around.

The brown pony was still watching Chombo. Its bright friendly eyes seemed to say, "Little boy, I can help you!"

Quickly, with a sudden smile, Chombo ran to the pony. Quietly he untied its bridle from a point of rock. He led the pony out into the middle of the cave, then flung his arms around it and laid his hot cheek against the pony's cool silky neck.

"Pony, pony," he whispered, "show me the way out!" Stepping back, he tapped the pony lightly. "Giddap!"

The pony hesitated. Then, with a toss of its pretty head, it walked straight toward the waterfall and stepped into the cloud of spray. Chombo followed, his heart beating fast. Where was the pony going? Suddenly it swung to the right, and now through the spray Chombo caught sight of a smooth rocky shelf leading out of the cave. Along the shelf and out of sight went the pony.

Chombo jumped for joy. The brown pony had shown him the way out! He wheeled round for a last look at the bandits, to make sure that he hadn't waked them.

What he saw was so startling that he nearly stepped backward into the waterfall.

A vanilla basket had tipped over. Brown beans had spilled out of it, and among the beans stood a little girl in a white dress. It was Mariquita! She had come with Chombo, after all!

Back at home, she had hidden herself in the vanilla basket. She had fallen asleep, and had slept through everything. Now she had waked up, and here she was. What was Chombo to do with her?

"Oh, oh," he groaned, "She'll wake the bandits for sure!"

Mariquita hadn't seen him yet. She was gazing, puzzled, at the bright waterfall. Then her lips began to tremble, and tears ran out of her eyes as she began to cry.

"I want to go home," moaned Mariquita.

Suddenly she saw Chombo. "Oh, there you are!" she cried gladly, and sprang toward him.

Chombo rushed to meet her. He put his hand over her mouth. "Hush, you'll wake the bandits!'

Mariquita's eyes grew round with alarm.

"We're in their hideaway," he whispered. "But don't be scared, I know the way out! Will you be quiet?"

Hand in hand they tiptoed past the bandits and up to the waterfall. Suddenly, just at the edge of the spray Mariquita hung back.

"Come on," he whispered. "It's all right, there's a shelf to walk on!"

The bandit chief sat up, rubbing his eyes. "Who are you?" he shouted.

"Come on!" shouted Chombo desperately.

He dragged her into the spray, pulled her along the shelf and out into the moonlight.

The pony was standing in a clump of trees.

The bandit chief rushed from the cave. "Come back here!" he shouted.

Chombo boosted Mariquita up on the pony. He scrambled up in front of her and shook the reins. "Giddap!"

The pony sprang forward. Chombo grabbed its neck, and Mariquita grabbed Chombo. Looking back, Chombo saw the bandit chief turn and dash under the waterfall.

"He's gone for his men!" said Chombo. "They'll be after us on horses! We'd better hide!"

Up above, along the brim of the valley, some banana trees nodded in the moonlight.

Chombo swung the pony that way. Up, up the steep bank and out of the valley they went. At the top, Chombo dismounted. Quickly he led the pony under a banana tree. The great leaves, as long as a man, hid all of them.

A moment later, the bandits galloped into sight. Without even a glance at the banana tree, they streamed on down

the valley and out of sight. Chombo smiled to himself. He waited. The pony stood quietly. Mariquita, with big eyes, sat silent on its back.

At last the bandits came back. As they rode by on their way back to their cave, Chombo heard one of them say, "I wish you hadn't let them get away. Suppose they find their way home, and tell the police!"

"Those children?" cried the bandit chief scornfully. "They don't know where they are. They'll wander around in circles all night and be lost in the forest by morning."

"Are they gone?" whispered Mariquita.

"Yes," said Chombo.

"Then you'll take me home now, won't you?"

Chombo didn't answer. He frowned at the forest, the dim and silent forest that rolled away on every side. The bandit chief was right. Chombo was lost!

He tied the pony to the banana tree, and lifted the little girl down. She lay down trustfully. He sat beside her, his back against the tree, hugging his knees. Soon she slept. But Chombo kept watch.

A Reward for Bravery

Hours passed, and now the moon was setting in the West. Slowly a change began. Eastward, behind the misty mountains, the sun was rising.

And with the light came the wind. Yes, a dawn wind sprang up in the West. It whispered through the forest; it reached the children. It blew and blew over Chombo, tossing his hair, breathing a message.

But Chombo was drowsy now. He sat dreaming of home, dreaming that he smelled the vanilla.

His eyes flew open. He did smell the vanilla!

A moment later, Mariquita woke up to find her brother dancing and jumping all around her.

"What is it?" she asked.

"We aren't lost any more! The wind! Smell the wind," he sang.

She sniffed carefully. Now she knew.

"Home!" said Mariquita.

The wind was sweet with vanilla. The wind came from home. It would lead them through the forest.

They started at once, riding together on the brown pony.

The sun was up now. It shone behind them, casting long shadows. It sparkled in the dew, and glowed in every color. The pony journeyed through a sea of green leaves. All the forest rang with bird songs. Chombo sang and whistled. Mariquita laughed, and the brown pony stepped along briskly.

The trees thinned. The long trail lay before them, the very same trail they had traveled the night before.

Mariquita clapped her hands. But Chombo said, "Listen!"

Gallop, gallop! Who was coming down the trail?

Hurriedly, Chombo rode the pony back into the forest. Dismounting, he slipped back to the trail and hid behind a tree to watch.

Gallop, gallop! A party of horsemen swept into sight. Out into the trail jumped Chombo, waving and shouting.

The party swung to a stop. Down sprang the Chief of Police of the Vanilla Village, seized Chombo, and swung him high in the air. All his men burst into a cheer.

"Were you looking for me?" cried Chombo, when he found himself on his feet again. "Then I know who sent you— my brothers!"

"Right!" said the Captain of Police. "The bandits took them by surprise last night. Before they could warn you, they were tied and gagged. All night they worked on the ropes. Finally they freed each other, and came straight to us. But I notice you didn't need any help," he added, smiling. "You escaped from the bandits all by yourself!"

"Yes," laughed Chombo.

"But there's bad news," said the Captain. "Your sister has disappeared. We fear she may

have hidden herself in another basket. Who knows where she is now?" He shook his head sadly.

Chombo said politely, "Will you wait just a minute?"

He dashed into the forest. When he ran back, he was leading the pony. And on the pony sat the lost little girl, laughing merrily.

What a surprise! Now it was little Mariquita's turn to be welcomed.

Then Chombo told them all about the cave behind the waterfall. "And maybe the bandits haven't waked up yet," he finished. "Why don't you go and see?"

"I think we'll do just that!" said the Captain. Then the police started for the waterfall.

Chombo and Mariquita followed the trail homeward.

The sun was high over the Vanilla Village, when the tall Captain of Police returned. Chombo was the first to see the Captain riding toward them up the narrow street.

"Here he comes!" he cried, waving.

The smiling Captain halted by the gate.

"Did you find the bandits' secret place?" cried Luis.

"Tell us about the fight!" begged Marcos.

"The fight was soon over," said the Captain, laughing. "We found them asleep in their cave, just as Chombo described. Right now they are safe in prison. The people of this village won't be robbed by bandits any more!'

Luis and Marcos were glad. Chombo was glad too, but something was troubling him. He ran to the brown pony and put his arms around it lovingly. "Please, does this pony still belong to the bandit chief?"

"Why, no," said the Captain.

"Doesn't he?" cried Chombo. "Then who owns him?"

"He belongs to the Vanilla Village."

Chombo turned away, hiding his face in the pony's thick mane.

"Oh, all right," he mumbled. "I only thought . . . Well, he helped me to escape from the bandits! He likes me, and I like him."

"Wait a minute!" cried the Captain. "I haven't finished. In the name of the whole Vanilla Village," he went on, "I hereby give this pony to you, Chombo, with thanks for your help in the capturing of the vanilla bandits!"

On Your Own

1. Why is the smell of vanilla such an important part of the story? Why do you think Chombo smelled vanilla when he was dreaming?

2. Pretend that you are Chombo telling the other Indian children about your adventure. What would you tell them about the following?
   (a) How you first knew you were captured by bandits
   (b) How the hideaway cave looked
   (c) How the pony helped you escape
   (d) How you and Mariquita became lost
   (e) How you found the way home
   (f) How you were found by the Captain of the Police

3. Make a picture of the bandits' cave.

SHIPS

By NANCY BYRD TURNER

Go out, good ships, across the tide,
Be brave to meet all weathers;
Make many a port, and fill each hold
With sky-blue silk and yellow gold
And pearls and peacock feathers.

The wind is in your shining sails,
Your keen prows cut the foam;
Sail very fast and very far,
Then turn, and by the Northern Star
Come steering safely home.

Ferdinand Magellan

By DOROTHY HEIDERSTADT

The world was round! People had known that since Columbus' famous voyage. But no one was daring enough to dream of sailing around the world—until Magellan did.

Magellan's Dream

The short, sturdy Portuguese boy stood on the pier at Lisbon. He was just one of a wildly cheering crowd. He was shouting with the best of them and waving his cap. His heart beat fast, his black eyes shone.

A battered ship was coming slowly into harbor. It was a wooden ship with tattered sails, the *San Gabriel,* last of the fleet with which Captain Vasco da Gama had sailed to India. Now the great captain was coming home. All his ships were lost but this one, and most of his crew was lost. But he had discovered a sea route to India, and this one weather-beaten ship was loaded with sandalwood, spices, and gold!

Those were great days for boys like young Ferdinand Magellan who stood cheering on the Lisbon pier. Explorer after explorer sailed for the fabulous Indies, for China, for the Spice Islands. When the ships came home, what wonderful stories the sailors could tell of far countries and strange sights! And what eager listeners the young Portuguese boys made! Each one of them dreamed of being a sailor and setting out for the Indies on his own some day.

Only a few years before, the Genoese captain, Columbus, had sailed away to the west, bound for a new passage to the Indies. He had discovered a land no man of his world had heard of before. Later Balboa had explored that land and found on the other side of it a new ocean. Amerigo Vespucci had given his name to the new continent—America.

"Someday," thought Magellan, "I'll be captain of a ship. Perhaps I shall discover a new part of the world myself."

It was a number of years before Ferdinand Magellan's dream came true. But he never lost sight of it. He became a sailor in the Portuguese navy, and studied geography and navigation. He sailed over all the seas of Asia, and when at last he returned home he was the captain of his own ship.

The world was round; everyone knew that.

"Suppose," thought Magellan, "a man should sail west instead of east to reach the Spice Islands. Since the world is a globe, someday he would reach the Islands. Then, if he continued and came on home, he would have sailed around the world!"

Magellan went to the King of Portugal, for he needed money and ships in order to carry out his great plan of trying to sail around the world. He promised the king that he would bring home a fortune in spices.

Spices were very important— they were used for preserving meat to keep it from spoiling. Spices made the meat and other foods taste better, too. Spices came from lands far away to the east, and they were as valuable as gold.

The King of Portugal would have liked to have a fortune in spices. But how was he to be sure that Magellan would return from such a strange voyage since he was planning to sail in the wrong direction at the very beginning? The king would have nothing to do with Magellan's wild plan.

Not discouraged, Magellan went to the King of Spain, who was young and venturesome. The king listened to the plan and gave Magellan the money he needed.

On September 20, 1519, a fleet of five small, battered, wooden ships sailed south-west-ward from Seville. They were the *San Antonio*, the *Conception*, the *Santiago*, the *Victoria* and the *Trinidad*. The ships and sails were old and had been patched many times. Their captain was Ferdinand Magellan.

Making a Dream Come True

Magellan stood on the deck of the flagship, *Trinidad*, and watched the shores of Spain slowly fading away. His dream was coming true. He was on his way to discover a passage around the world.

Far to the west lay the great continent of South America.

"Somewhere," thought Magellan, "at the southernmost tip of that continent, there must be a strait leading from the Atlantic Ocean to the China seas." Magellan was sure that China lay just on the other side of South America. He was determined to find that strait.

A light was kept burning on the high deck of the *Trinidad,* so the other ships would always be able to keep it in sight.

For a time there was fine weather. Then storms began to batter the small wooden ships.

The sailors muttered angrily against the voyage and the low pay and the food, which was neither very good nor very plentiful. But Magellan refused to be discouraged.

In November the fleet reached the coast of Brazil. The taste of sweet pineapples which the natives brought to the ships cheered the sailors. They began to trade with the natives—a knife for several chickens, a comb for a basket full of fish, a little bell for a basket full of sweet potatoes.

There had been no rain along the Brazilian coast for some months. Now that Magellan's ships had come, the rains came too. The simple natives thought that the white strangers had brought the cooling rains with them. And more to be wondered at were all these things the strangers had brought: knives, bells, looking glasses, and bundles of bright-red cloth.

Magellan liked the friendly natives and wished to convert them to Christianity. The Christmas season seemed a very good time to do it. The natives were taught to fold their hands, kneel, and pray.

Magellan sailed on and came to the mouth of a river. He believed that this must be the strait he was looking for—the one which led to the Chinese seas. The five ships sailed confidently into the river. But after two days they had to turn back, for the water was fresh. They knew that fresh water could come only from inland. They must find salt water.

Storm after storm hammered the ships as they sailed along. Magellan had to find a harbor where the ships could spend the winter. When they were in harbor he put the crew on scanty rations. Again the men began to complain and wanted to return to Spain. A mutiny broke out, but Magellan stopped it. He was determined not to give up and go home.

One day a giant came down to the shore. He danced about and sang. He was so tall that Magellan's tallest men came only to his waist. The giant was good-natured and friendly. His face was painted red and yellow. He brought his friends —other giants like himself— down to the shore to look at the big ships with the little men aboard. Because these giants had such big feet, the sailors called them "Patagones." *Patagãos* means big feet in Portuguese. The giants' country

near the southern tip of South America is still called Patagonia.

When spring came the fleet sailed out of the harbor and to the south. Soon Magellan saw a deep channel. He sent two ships to explore it. They found the water to be salt. Magellan felt sure that he had at last found the passage he was looking for—the passage leading to the Chinese seas.

For five weeks the ships sailed through a maze of channels at the southern tip of South America. Later this passage was to be named the Strait of Magellan. The sailors were displeased and very angry. They pleaded continually to return to Spain. One ship was wrecked. Another ship deserted and headed back the way they had come. But Magellan went on with the rest.

Then at last they sailed out into a wide stretch of water. Magellan was happy, for any day now he expected to see the coast of China. But day after day passed and there was only the wide, calm sea.

"How big the world is!" thought Magellan. "Here is an ocean we never knew of. It must be a new ocean. I will call it Pacific because it is so peaceful."

It was tiresome, sailing on and on over that enormous sea. Now and then, a desert island was sighted. But there were no natives ashore to bring fresh fruit to trade with the sailors. When at last they landed in a group of islands they found that the natives were thieves, so Magellan named the islands the Ladrones—Thieves' Islands.

Fresh food from these islands made the sailors more cheerful, however. So the ships moved on. After sailing on the new ocean for ninety-eight days, Magellan came to the islands later to be known as the Philippines. The natives were friendly and gentle. They brought oranges, bananas and coconuts to the sailors.

It was a pleasant life on the islands, after the long, hungry sea voyage. Magellan lingered there, converting the natives to Christianity and collecting tribute for the King of Spain. He made friends with some of the native kings.

One king who was Magellan's special friend complained that he was having trouble with another native king. Magellan said that he would attack the enemy king and overcome him.

Magellan and his men met thousands of determined natives armed with bows, arrows, and spears. In the fight which followed, Magellan was killed.

Another man became captain of the fleet and sailed on to the Spice Islands. One by one the little ships had been lost. In 1522 the little *Victoria* alone

sailed slowly into Seville harbor. She was loaded with spices, ginger, sandalwood and birds of paradise. She had sailed completely around the world. But her great captain, who had fought for so long to make the dream come true, was dead.

Only eighteen men survived the long voyage around the world. The new captain received great honors and riches.

But it had been Magellan's courage and determination that made the long voyage possible. To Ferdinand Magellan goes the honor of having dreamed of sailing around the world and of leading that first tremendous voyage almost to its end.

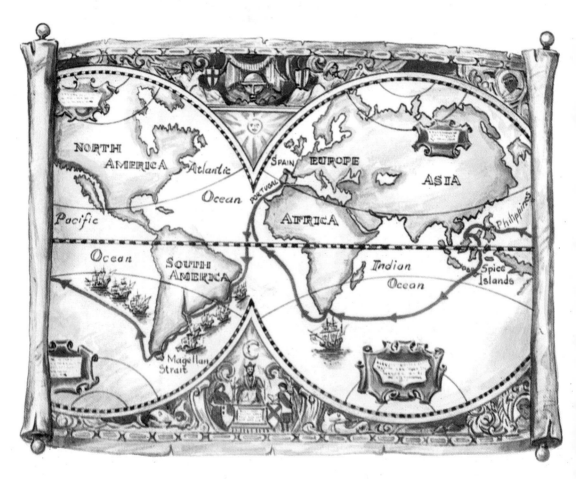

On Your Own

1. What was Magellan's great plan? Why did the King of Portugal refuse to help him? What king did help Magellan? Why was it important to make trips to the Spice Islands? What were Magellan's greatest problems on the trip? How did his dream come true?

2. How did Patagonia and the Ladrones Islands get their names? What does each name mean? Find the following places on a globe or map and tell how the first two got their names.
   (a) Pacific Ocean   (c) Spain
   (b) Strait of Magellan   (d) Portugal

3. Find statements in the story to prove that Magellan was:
   (a) Brave and bold
   (b) A good leader
   (c) Determined to follow his plan

IF I WERE A ONE-LEGGED PIRATE

By MILDRED PLEW MEIGS

If I were a one-legged pirate
   Ga-lumping around on a peg,
I'd flourish my pistol and fire it;
   Then, sure as my right wooden leg,
I'd buy me a three-decker galleon
   With cannon to port and to lee,
And wearing the king's medallion,
   I'd head for a tropical sea!
Roaring a rough Ha-ha!   Ha-ho!
   Roving the routes of old,
Over the billows we would go,
   Sweeping the seas for gold!
     Plying the lane
     Of the Spanish Main
      For Gold!
       Gold!
        Gold!

If I were a one-legged pirate
 Ga-lumping around after loot,
I'd flourish my pistol and fire it;
 Then, sure as my red leather boot,
I'd buy me a three-decker galleon
 With cannon to thunder a mile,
And bucking the sea like a stallion
 I'd head for a tropical isle!
Roaring a rough Ha-ha! Ha-ho!
 Chanting a chantey bold,
Over the billows we would blow,
 Sweeping the seas for gold!
  Plying the lane
  Of the Spanish Main
   For Gold!
   Gold!
   Gold!

But since I was not born a pirate
 Ga-lumping around on a stick;
And since my toy gun when I fire it
 Gives but a little toy click;
Pretending my boat is a galleon,
 My pond is a tropical sea,
I'll play I'm an old rapscallion,
 But really I won't hurt a flea.
Roaring my small Ha-ha! Ha-ho!
 Saying I'm someone bold,
Over the duck pond I will go,
 Roving the routes of old;
  Plying the pond
  And the stream beyond
   For Gold!
   Gold!
   Gold!

Following the Path of Magellan

By CAPTAIN EDWARD L. BEACH, USN

When the *Triton,* the first submarine to travel submerged all the way around the world, left on its trip, many of the crew left families behind them. The captain of the ship, Captain Beach, had two boys, aged twelve and ten, and a little girl, seven. When the ship's long submerged trip was nearly over, he wrote them this letter.

U.S.S. *Triton*
1 May 1960
At Sea

Dear Children:

It has been two and a half months since I said good-bye to you, last February, and I suppose you have been wondering where your Dad has been all this time. Maybe you have also been wondering why you have not been receiving any mail from me. Well, the truth is, we have been on a long, secret and wonderful voyage. It is now nearly finished, and this letter will tell you something about it, but I shall have to be my own mailman and bring it home to you myself.

200

On February 16th, 1960, the *Triton* left Groton, Connecticut, where she had been built, and went to sea with secret orders. I was the only one who knew where we were going, but I could not tell the crew until after we were on our way. All I could say was that we were going on a long cruise, and that they should be ready for anything. Submarine sailors are usually ready for anything anyway, so this was all right with them. We put enough food on board the ship to last us 120 days, and if we were careful and did not eat as much as we wanted there would be enough food to last us more than half a year.

After we had been at sea for a day and everything was working all right, I made a speech to the whole crew and told them that we were going to go around the world submerged. Everyone was excited, but some of them, of course, wondered how they would feel after

spending three months under water. I must admit I wondered the same thing myself. It was winter when we left home, and it was going to be nearly summer when we got back.

The *Triton*, as you know, is an atomic submarine. The same tremendous power which made the atom bomb makes steam to drive her engines. A little piece of uranium smaller than a basketball (but so heavy that you couldn't lift it) has enough power in it to drive the *Triton* completely around the world and more besides.

Before atomic power for submarines was perfected, submerged submarines had to run their electric motors by means of storage batteries. These batteries are exactly like the one in our car, only bigger. As you know, if you run these batteries for a long while, they will run down and have to be recharged. A submarine would have to come up and start its diesel engines to charge up the batteries again.

Submarines could not run their diesel engines while submerged because, besides fuel, they have to have lots of air. All engines in the world, except the atomic engines, need air before they can run, no matter what kind of fuel they use. I have shown you that our automobile has a carburetor which mixes air with the gasoline, and that the used-up air goes out the exhaust pipe. Steamships use oil or coal to make steam, but to burn the oil or the coal there has to be air, and the used-up air goes out the smokestack.

But the atomic engine does not need oxygen or air, so it will work just as well under water as anywhere else. Thus, for the first time, the submarine became able to go long distances and stay down a very long time. One of the purposes of our trip was to see how long a crew could stay under water, and how far they could go. Also, we wanted to see if we could go entirely around the world without having anyone know where we were.

Magellan was not really the first man to travel around the world, because he died before the trip was finished; but he is given the honor because he was the one who planned the trip and led it most of the way.

Triton's route

Magellan's route

Since we were also going to try to go around the world, the Navy called our trip "Project Magellan," and when we began to plan our route it was easy to see that we had to follow almost exactly the same route that Magellan followed. The only thing was that we did not try to go through the Strait of Magellan. To do so we would have to get permission from the Republic of Chile, since the Strait goes through that country, and our trip would no longer have been a secret. Besides, the Strait of Magellan is so near the bottom of South America that it didn't make much difference anyway.

Naturally, I hardly expected not to have any problems during the trip. The biggest problem we had was one which I didn't expect at all. We had a Navy doctor with us and he had enough medicines to take care of practically any sort of illness. The one thing we couldn't be ready for was the kind of sickness that overtook one of our

crew, who had an attack of kidney stones on the way to Cape Horn. The doctor on board could only give him shots so that it would not hurt, but he couldn't do anything about the kidney stones. Sometimes they go away by themselves, but when these did not, the doctor advised me that we had to get help.

This was, of course, a big problem because if we came up and took him into some harbor, this would ruin our submerged record. Everybody on board was very much upset at the thought that this man's sickness might wreck our cruise, yet at the same time they knew that

he had to be taken care of. Fortunately, I happened to know of a U.S. cruiser, the *Macon*, which was in South America at this time and we sent a message asking if the *Macon* could meet us at sea and take off the sick man. When the answer came back that the *Macon* would meet us, I knew that our problem was solved.

The *Triton* and the *Macon* met at midnight, and we didn't actually surface, but instead we got the top of the *Triton* just high enough out of water to open the top hatch and get the sick man and two helpers outside. He was all bundled up with life preservers, and when the boat from the *Macon* came alongside, he stepped from the top of the *Triton* right into the boat and only got his feet wet. Since the *Triton* had not actually come all the way up, our submerged record was still safe.

A few days later we passed by Cape Horn and I had everybody in the ship look at it. If a sailor passes Cape Horn and sees it accidentally, he is supposed to have bad luck (usually a shipwreck right then and there). But if you see Cape Horn on purpose it means good luck will follow you all your time at sea. So I ordered everybody to get up and see Cape Horn through the periscope.

The only trouble with this was that I had forgotten how long it would take everybody in the ship to go to the periscope and take a look, and we had to turn around and go by Cape Horn twice more to give everyone a chance. Perhaps you have seen photographs of Cape Horn. It is a huge, solid rock with a few scrubby bushes on top and rather worn away by the water at the bottom. It is at the very bottom of South America and is one of the famous landmarks of the sea.

After passing Cape Horn we sailed out into the Pacific and

the next place we passed was Easter Island. Poor Magellan never saw Easter Island, which was a shame, because his ships had run out of food. If they had seen Easter Island they might have been able to stop for food and water, but they sailed by just a few miles away and didn't even know it was there.

I was also interested in Easter Island because hundreds of years ago some people lived there who carved many great figures, some of them buried so that only the heads can be seen. I wanted to see one of them, and finally, after searching for quite a long time, I did see one. Unfortunately it was too far away to get a good picture.

After Easter Island, it was a long trip across the Pacific Ocean to Guam, an American island not far from the Philippine Islands. This was the first place Magellan was able to get food, and many of his men had starved to death during their terrible trip all the way from South America.

One of the *Triton's* crew, a sailor named Carbullido, was born on Guam. Fourteen years ago he had enlisted in the Navy and every month he had sent most of his pay home to his parents, but this was the first time he had ever returned home himself. Now here we were, at his home island, and we couldn't let him out of our submarine. All we could do was to go as close to his home town, Agat by name, as we could. So *Triton* went into Agat Bay, and the whole time we were there Carbullido looked through the periscope at his home. Little did anyone in the city of Agat realize that out there in the water, just a little distance away, one of their home-town boys had come back for a look! Carbullido said that the town was very different from the way it was when he remembered it, but he could see his old church and the school he went to as a boy. His parents had built a new house there, partly with money that he had sent, and

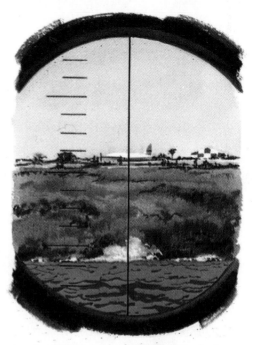

Carbullido was pretty sure he could see it.

When we finally had to leave, I promised Carbullido that somehow we would get him back home for Christmas, and we will, too!

After we left Guam, we went to the Philippine Islands, where the daring Magellan lost his life. This sad event took place near the city of Cebu, which is on a large island also called Cebu and is one of the important cities in the Philippine Islands. Cebu welcomed Magellan with great friendliness, but when Magellan tried

207

to help the people of Cebu against their warlike neighbors on the island of Mactan, he and his men were attacked by over a thousand Filipinos; and Magellan, fighting to help his men escape, was killed. Many years later a monument was built in his memory at the very spot where he died, and we were coming to see if we could see it through our periscope.

On the 1st of April, *Triton* entered Magellan Bay and, cruising close to the shore, saw the monument made to the famous but unfortunate explorer who first found the way to sail around the world. It was here, too, that the only person who saw the *Triton* during the entire trip came upon us. It was a native in a dugout canoe who thought he saw a fish jumping in the water and, paddling closer to it, saw our periscope while we were photographing the monument.

He didn't know that it was a periscope, however, and probably thought it was the fin of a sea monster. So he paddled away as fast as he could, looking back fearfully to see if the sea monster was chasing him.

After leaving Magellan Bay, we steamed down through the Sulu Sea, the Celebes Sea, Makassar Strait, and Lombok Strait and finally into the Indian Ocean.

We rounded the Cape of Good Hope on Easter Sunday and then steamed up the length of the Atlantic Ocean again to St. Peter and St. Paul Rocks, which we reached on the 25th of April, having passed by there before on the 24th of February. But, though there had been 61 days since we had been there, we had counted only 60.

It might interest you to know that it was one of Magellan's crew, a man named Pigafetta, who first discovered that you have to add or subtract a day when you go around the world. He kept a very careful diary, and when he got back to Spain he found to his amazement that he had counted one less day

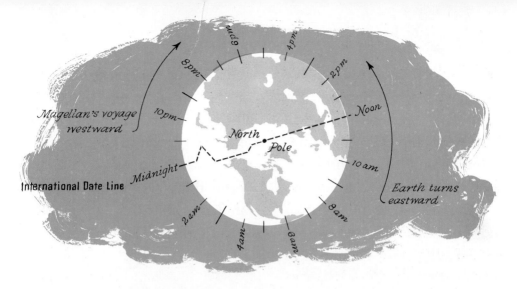

This diagram shows the 24 time zones of the world.
When Magellan and his men traveled westward,
they "lost" an hour every time they crossed a time zone.
When his men reached home from the trip around
the world, they had "lost" 24 hours, or one day.

than the people in Spain. So he went back over his diary and checked it very carefully, but he could not find out what was wrong.

Finally he went to a very learned man and, after much discussion, they realized that by traveling once around the world Pigafetta had passed by the sun one less time than the people who had stayed home in Spain! This is because the earth rotates, and, of course, Spain went by the sun once each rotation, or once a day. But Pigafetta saw the sun one less time because he went westward, chasing the sun. If he had gone around to the eastward, he would have seen it one more time than the people who stayed home.

As I write this, we have received orders to surface off the coast of Delaware, where a helicopter will come and bring me to Washington, D.C. so that I can report completion of the trip.

Our trip altogether will have been 36,000 nautical miles, or about 42,000 land miles. We shall have been submerged for eighty-four days and *Triton* will be the first ship ever to go completely around the world entirely submerged. I am as proud as I can be of my men and my ship. No other ship and no other crew could have done better.

Of course, the most wonderful thing of all is the feeling we all have that we have done something worthwhile for our country. The next most wonderful thing will be to see our families again.

Until then,

Love,
Dad

On Your Own

1. Why did the Navy call the *Triton's* trip "Project Magellan"? What were the two purposes of the *Triton's* trip? What was one of the problems? Were the purposes carried out? How did these differ from Magellan's purpose?
2. What is the meaning of each of these words? Find out from the story or look them up in the glossary.

    (a) submarine
    (b) atomic power
    (c) submerged
    (d) periscope
    (e) explorer
    (f) uranium
3. What was the power used to run the engine of the *Triton*? Could the *Triton* have made the trip completely submerged if it had used oil, coal, storage batteries, or sails? Explain your answer.
4. "*Triton* Follows Magellan's Wake," National Geographic Magazine, November, 1960, is also written by Captain Beach and has many good pictures of the trip.

A SONG OF GREATNESS

By MARY AUSTIN

When I hear the old men
Telling of heroes,
Telling of great deeds
Of ancient days,
When I hear that telling
Then I think within me
I too am one of these.
When I hear the people
Praising great ones,
Then I know that I too
Shall be esteemed,
I too when my time comes
Shall do mightily.

Thinking It Through

1. On a globe or world map, trace the routes followed by:
   (a) Magellan and his men
   (b) Captain Beach and the *Triton*

   Compare the two journeys. How were they alike? How were they different? If possible, get an outline map of the world and use two different colors to trace the two routes. You may wish to make your map a picture map as well.

2. It had been sixty-one days since the *Triton* had left its base, but the crew counted only sixty days. Can you explain why? Who discovered the answer to this strange problem long ago? You may be interested in finding out more about the reasons for gaining or losing a day in going around the world.

3. Compare "Jack-O'-Lantern" and "Prairie Fire."
   (a) In what part of the United States did Jonathan's family live? Ilse's family?
   (b) How did the members of each family show their love and consideration for each other? Of which family would you rather have been a member? Why?

4. Look up *vanilla* in an encyclopedia. Find out how the beans are made ready for market. What is vanilla used for? Be ready to tell some facts about vanilla.

5. Choose the story character that you think was bravest and boldest. Write a report about this character.

DREAMS

By Marchette Chute

Once I was a pirate,
A savage, slashing pirate;
I flew the skull and cross-bones
   and I stamped upon the deck.

Once I was a camel
(A handsome sort of camel),
And ambled in a caravan
   with jewels around my neck.

Once I was a dancer,
And once a necromancer,
I even was a Viking
   with a helmet on my head.

I might have been a carrot
Or a strange Brazilian parrot
If someone hadn't wakened me
   and pulled me

        out

          of

            bed.

Denis and the Cloud

By ELIZABETH ENRIGHT

Denis, a quick-thinking boy, used magic from the sky
to make his wish come true.

Living in the Desert

Father and Mother lived in the house, if you could call it a house. It had only two rooms and a poor excuse for a kitchen.

Still it was a house, with a door and some windows, and a floor to step on. But Denis had a tent. It was very small and sat close beside the house. Still it was a tent, with no door, no windows and only the hard desert earth to step on. Denis liked it better than any house in the world. At night when there was a moon the canvas glowed dimly all about him, and the huge sahuaro cactus that grew near by laid its long black shadow overhead.

Every night at the same time the wind woke up like an animal and came roaring softly across the desert. Under its force the tent would flap and flutter and bulge. Sometimes Denis would wake up for a minute and listen to the big sea sound of the wind, and the distant scary crying of the coyotes, and the near scratchy noise of the desert mouse who liked to eat nuts under the bed. Denis would lie there and be a little frightened, but mostly proud that he was hearing sounds such as these instead of the kind that most children hear at night: feet going up and downstairs, cars in the street, or the radio in another house.

In the morning when he woke up it was always calm and still, and the sun was blazing over the mountains. What had happened to the wind?

For six months now they had lived in the desert. Father had been ill when they came out here, but already he was so much better that he spoke of going home soon. Denis didn't like to think of going home. The desert was a marvelous new world full of danger and surprises. And after this a back yard would be about as interesting as a dish of peas.

Living on the place, besides themselves, there were half a dozen chickens, a pair of goats named Nelly and Joe—nobody knew why—and Filibuster, the donkey.

Father and Mother had a very old Ford to ride in, but Denis had Filibuster all to himself. He was a tiny barrel-shaped burro with a rough coat, a sleepy, wise face, and ears like a jack rabbit's. He looked as if he should spend his

life being petted and protected, but actually he was as strong as an ox, and when he opened his mouth to bray he sounded like a five-alarm fire. You could have heard him in the next county.

Every day Denis went exploring on Filibuster's back and found him a good companion. He could climb any mountain, follow any trail however narrow, and he had a strong taste for adventure just as Denis had.

Off Exploring

One morning Denis woke up earlier than usual. The sky was full of light, but the sun had not yet risen above the big mountain that sheltered the little camp. The shadow of the mountain was cold and deep like a lake, and Denis shivered when he got out of bed. He hurried into his icy clothes with his teeth chattering. But when he had stamped around and slapped his arms and said, "Gee, it's cold!" a few times,

he began to feel better and went outside.

All along the horizon there were parades of high mountains with wicked-looking cliffs. In the morning, like this, they were always a shining pink, but they changed their colors many times a day. They could be blue, or violet, or golden, or fire red. From the mountains behind the house to the ones across the valley it was thirty miles. Just behind them and stretching far away to the right and left, big as an ocean, lay the desert. It looked like no other place in the world. All the things that grew in it had queer shapes and queer colors. The sahuaro cactuses were the tallest ones; high as churches, some of them, and hundreds of years old. Denis had heard that sahuaros exactly like these were growing in the world during the days of the dinosaurs. "It was a funny thing," he thought while he brushed his teeth out of a tumbler, "a dinosaur would look all right in the desert. He

would look as if he belonged there, even now."

Next Denis built the fire in the outdoor oven. Nelly and Joe hurried toward him on their clattering hoofs and sniffed at his pockets hopefully. "M-a-a-a," said Nelly in a thin complaining voice and gave him a look with her cold yellow eye.

"Go away," replied Denis, "and the next time you eat a half a tube of my toothpaste there's going to be trouble."

The chickens came pecking, and looked at him curiously under their red combs. Everyone was hungry. Even Filibuster tied in his shelter was braying for food. Denis decided to surprise his mother and start the coffee. He climbed into the kitchen window, unhooked the pot, put in the coffee, and turned and banged his leg on the ice-cream freezer. That freezer! It was halfway between a joke and something very sad. They hadn't known when they moved out here that they would never be able to get ice. Everything that had to be kept cold was hung in the well on the end of a long rope. But as for ice cream! It was something you wished for, thought about on hot days, but didn't believe.

Denis went down to the well and hauled up a bucket of water, filled the pot, and took it back to the fire. His mother looked out of the window, very sleepy, pushing her hair out of her eyes.

"Denis, how wonderful!" she said. "But I'll do the rest. You take care of the birds and beasts."

So Denis fed the animals and gave them water as he did every day.

"Breakfast!" called his mother at last, and Denis ran.

He was as hungry as anyone else. That was another thing about this place. You ate out of doors, and everything tasted better.

"Be careful," said his father, watching Denis at work on his third egg. "You'll be giving Filibuster a swayback."

"He has the beginning of one already," said Mother dreamily. "He's not a proud animal anyway. Not with his kind of looks."

"He's a pretty good donkey," remarked Denis.

"Looks aren't everything," Mother agreed. "I like his funny face. And I don't know how we'd get along without him."

After breakfast Denis hauled water for the kitchen, milked the goat, and collected eggs which he found in the strangest places. There was even one in the back seat of the Ford. It was late in the morning when he and Filibuster were ready to depart. He could hear the

stuttering noise of his father's typewriter under the paloverde tree, and his mother was busy indoors.

Filibuster wore a fancy Spanish saddle with a high horn. Denis looped a lasso over it. He wasn't much good at lassoing things yet, but he liked the way it looked. He had a saddlebag, too, that the harness man had given him. It came in handy. There was always something in it when he and Filibuster came home; stones that looked as if they might have gold in them, or dried roots for firewood, or the bleached bones of animals.

His mother leaned out of the kitchen window, waving a package. "Lunch for you, Denis," she called. "And two lumps of sugar for Filibuster's dessert."

"Wonderful," said Denis, stowing the package of lunch in his saddlebag.

"Where are you off to?" asked his mother.

Denis said: "Today we're going to find out about that mountain over there. The one that looks sort of like a buffalo sitting down."

"All right," said his mother. "Come back with no bones broken, please. And I hope you'll bring something interesting home with you."

"I'll try," promised Denis, beginning to feel excited as he climbed aboard Filibuster.

It might be today he would discover a silver mine or a dinosaur. You never could tell.

The Storm

Filibuster clip-clopped comfortably along, taking his time and looking where he was going. He had to. Everything that grew in the desert was covered with prickles. Tiny chipmunks with their tails straight up in the air hustled out of the way, and scorpions skimmed over the rocks as though run by electricity. It began to be very hot. A ribbon of heat hung over the desert.

"It's going to be summer soon," said Denis. Filibuster flapped an ear. "Snakes 'll be coming out any day now." Filibuster did not reply.

They reached the foot of their mountain and wound about it searching for a trail of some sort. It didn't look much like a buffalo when you got too close to it. They started up the uneven path of a wash, made by the force of forgotten cloudbursts, until they came to what looked as if it had once been a trail. It wound steeply around the mountain. Filibuster panted and scrambled over the stones, and the harness leather creaked. The sun burned fiercely; Denis could feel his shirt stuck to his back like a wet rag. Was it only this morning that he'd been stamping his feet to keep warm?

Gradually they mounted high above the desert. There it lay all spread out below them. And far away to the left Denis could see a small toy house and a tent no bigger than a lump of sugar.

"Stop! Whoa!" said Denis suddenly.

The thought of sugar had reminded him. He got down and took their lunch from the saddlebag. Filibuster had his tied onto his nose, and Denis ate his right out of the paper. There was no nonsense about forks or napkins.

As he ate Denis looked up at the sky. There was a big lumpy cloud like a fist rising above the mountain, and against its glittering whiteness an eagle wheeled and drifted, wheeled and drifted, as if he had been doing nothing else for seven thousand years.

"I hope it isn't going to rain," Denis said. Filibuster sighed heavily.

As they continued along the forgotten trail the air grew cooler. The fist of cloud unclosed like a giant hand and spread itself across the sun. But only the mountain was in shadow. Below them the desert burned with light.

"Filibuster!" cried Denis suddenly. "Stop! Whoa! Gee whiz!"

Filibuster stopped, little interested, but Denis sat perfectly still, staring at a huge red rock beside the trail. There were pictures on it. Here in the wilderness, on this particular rock among all the scattered thousands, somebody had made wonderful pictures, sharp and clear and exciting. There were running deer with long antlers, a man with a bow and arrow, a scorpion, and a snake looped up in circles. And there was a strange design that must have had a magic meaning once.

"How long since anyone's seen this?" thought Denis.

He wondered how many hundred years had passed since an Indian had stood here making pictures of the things that he thought beautiful or important. There weren't many Indians around any more. They lived on the reservations mostly and made bracelets and rings and blankets and other things to sell in stores.

"I must show this to Father," said Denis, and rode on.

Now the big cloud settled down on the mountain like a huge nesting bird. It cast a dark shadow, and its breath was cold; but all the rest of the world was bright with sunshine still.

"I wonder why it picked this mountain?" said Denis, feeling impatient. "We aren't going to let it stop us anyway."

But suddenly the storm broke and it began to pour. And then the rain started thumping him on the back and bouncing off

his hat like marbles, and he realized that it wasn't rain at all. It was hail.

"Ow, it's like gun shot!" complained Denis.

There was an opening in the rocks ahead and he steered Filibuster towards it. The hail grew bigger and hit harder.

"Like cannon balls, I mean," squealed Denis.

Filibuster broke into a trot and Denis slid from his back and dove into the little cave. It was only big enough to hold Denis, and Filibuster's head and forefeet. The rest of the poor donkey remained outside and was whacked hard by the hail.

"It'll be over soon," said Denis hopefully, patting Filibuster's nose.

But while it lasted it was awful. The hail was so enormous that it banged and bounced as it landed. Tons of it seemed to be falling from the sky. Denis was cold, and Filibuster was most uncomfortable.

Magic from the Sky

After what seemed a long time the storm lessened and the light returned slowly. The wicked cloud drifted away looking woolly and harmless, and Denis turning his head caught the first sight of a second companion in the cave. On a rock shelf close to his shoulder, he saw the leathery loops of a rattlesnake still stupid with cold and sleep. Without knowing that he moved, Denis found himself outside the cave with Filibuster.

"I wonder if my hair's standing on end," said Denis in a quiet voice and took his hat off to find out. It felt just the same as usual, but it was a few minutes before Denis did.

The mountainside was covered with hailstones the size of pigeon eggs. Denis, still shaking a little, picked up one of the hailstones and licked it. It tasted of winter.

"We ought to be able to do something with these," he said thoughtfully. "But what?"

Filibuster looked sleepily across the desert and switched his tail.

"Jiminy!" shouted Denis. "Why didn't I think of it before?"

Working like lightning he opened the saddlebag and began scooping up hailstones quickly before they could melt. At last the saddlebag bulged and the hat was heavy on his arm.

"Come on now," he said excitedly. "Be careful and don't slip. I'll walk so it'll be easier."

He took Filibuster's bridle in his free hand and together they picked their way among the slippery hailstones. It took a long time to reach the foot of the mountain. The sun burned fiercely once again and Denis kept saying anxiously, "Oh, if only they don't melt."

It was strange, but when they reached the level desert there was no hail on the ground at all, no dampness even. Denis got back on Filibuster again. He balanced the hat in front of him.

"Go like lightning," he commanded, and Filibuster ran.

He galloped all the way home with the saddlebag whacking him in the sides at every step. Denis rode up to the house with a dashing air. His mother came out to meet him.

"Father's gone for a walk," she said. Then she caught sight of the hat and the bulging saddlebag. "What in the world have you brought?"

"Look!" said Denis.

"Ice," said his mother, puzzled.

"For ice cream," added Denis.

"Oh, Denis, oh, darling," cried his mother, beginning to laugh. "Where on earth did you get it? Did you dig it up like gold? Or did you find it hanging on a bush like fruit?"

"No, Mother," laughed Denis. "It just fell from the sky."

They hurried then. His mother mixed condensed milk, and sugar, and vanilla, while he packed the ice-cream freezer with hailstones. They then took turns cranking. At the end of twenty minutes they were both hot and red in the face, but the handle wouldn't go around any more, and they knew the ice cream was ready.

His mother looked out of the window. "We're just in time!"

Father had returned from his walk. He was hot, and his face

looked tired. He sighed as he sat down in his chair under the paloverde tree. Denis took him the first dish of ice cream, white as snow and beautiful. His father looked at it. "I don't believe it," he said.

"But it's real!" exclaimed Denis.

"Can't be," said his father decidedly. "Here, let me taste it."

He took a spoonful. Then he smiled and shook his head.

"It's real, all right. Who says there's no magic left on earth? Who says there's no magic in the sky? I was thinking, as I walked home, that I'd be willing to spend my last nickel for an ice-cream cone."

So they had a party under the paloverde tree, and there was enough ice cream for three times around for everyone.

"And if we all have stomachaches tonight," said Mother, "it was worth it!"

On Your Own

1. List the sounds that Denis could hear on the desert at night. Then list some of the sounds that you hear at night.

2. Compare your home, food, means of travel, and ways of having fun with those of Denis.

3. Pretend you are Denis writing a letter to a friend in the city. Choose one of the following to write about.
   (a) Describe Filibuster and tell what he could do.
   (b) Describe the Indian pictures on the rock.
   (c) Describe the adventure with Filibuster during the storm on the mountain.
   (d) Describe the experience of making ice cream.

MINNIE

By ELEANOR FARJEON

Minnie can't make her mind up,
Minnie can't make up her mind!
  They ask her at tea,
  "Well, what shall it be?"
  And Minnie says, "Oh,
  Muffins, please! no,
  Sandwiches—yes,
  Please, egg-and-cress—
  I mean a jam one,
Or is there another kind?
  Never mind!
        Cake
  Is what I will take,
The sort with the citron-rind,
  Or p'r'aps the iced one—
  Or is there a spiced one,
Or is there the currant kind?"
  When tea is done
  She hasn't begun,
She's always the one behind,
Because she can't make her mind up,
Minnie *can't* make up her mind!

229

Johnny and His Mule

By ELLIS CREDLE

Johnny bought a mule on Trade Day, but he found
out that it was a balker. What could he do with a
stubborn mule?

What Will Make Him Go?

Away up in the Great Smoky
Mountains there is a town
called Horny Hollow. It is not
a very large town, and the great
mountains standing up all
around make it seem very small
indeed. There are no more
than twenty houses there, a
courthouse, several stores, a
church, and a schoolhouse.

To this little schoolhouse
came all the children in the
town and a little mountain boy
named Johnny. Johnny lived
far back in the hills, a long, long
way from town.

He had to get up very early,
when the cocks were crowing
for the sunrise, to get to school
on time. But in spite of the

long walk over the mountains, he was never late for school.

The town children might hustle into the school yard as the last bell was ringing. They might catch the end of the line as it was marching into the building. They might even tip-toe fearfully into the room after classes had started. But never Johnny! He was always in his place as the line marched in and in his proper seat when classes began. In the fall, in the winter, and in the spring, it was always the same. Johnny was always on time.

But one day, toward the end of the school year, Johnny was late! The last bell rang—Johnny was not there! Nine o'clock came—and still no Johnny. Ten o'clock rolled around, half past ten, and not a sign of Johnny.

It was so very late now, the children and the teacher began to wonder what had happened. Perhaps Johnny was sick or perhaps he had fallen over the steep mountainside on the way to school. But half an hour

later, at eleven o'clock, there was a shuffle-shuffle outside the door. It opened slowly and Johnny creaked into the room.

"Why, Johnny!" cried the teacher. "It's eleven o'clock! Why are you so late?"

"I-I-I just couldn't help it, Miss Mary!" stuttered Johnny, and he looked as though he might cry at any moment.

"But tell me, what happened?" asked Miss Mary.

"I got into town early this morning, Miss Mary," began Johnny, "in plenty of time for

school, but I stopped for a minute in the town square to watch the auction sale."

Everyone knew about the auction. It was held every Friday, and the mountaineers called it "Trade Day." They came in from all the surrounding hills and ranges bringing anything they had on hand which they wanted to trade or sell. Handmade chairs, baskets, turkeys, jackknives, horses, preserves, feather pillows, anything and everything went on sale in the town square on Friday.

"And so," continued Johnny, "while I was standing there, an old mule was put up to be sold. The auctioneer began shouting, 'What am I offered for this mule? What am I bid? What am I bid?'

"Nobody would begin the bidding, and so, just to get the sale started, I called out, 'I bid five cents!' I thought surely somebody would bid higher because mules usually cost a lot of money. But nobody did, and so they gave me the mule!

"And there I stood, Miss Mary, holding the mule by the halter. I didn't know what to do with him. About the only thing I could think of was to take him along to school with me. So I started out.

"I soon found out why nobody wanted that mule. After we had gone about a block he stopped stock-still. I tried every way to get him to go along, but he wouldn't budge an inch. He was a balker! Lots of other people tried to make him go, but no sir! That mule wouldn't go until he felt like it. After a while, all by himself, he took a notion to start. He walked another block and then he balked again. Miss Mary, honest-to-goodness, it took me two hours to get that critter four blocks to the schoolhouse! That's why I'm late, honest-to-goodness!"

"Why, Johnny!" exclaimed Miss Mary. "I never heard such a tale!"

"If you don't believe it, Miss Mary, just look out the window," replied Johnny.

The teacher gazed through the window and so did all the children. There, tied to a tree, was a mule. His head hung down and his large ears drooped sadly. There was no doubt about it, Johnny's tale was true.

Lessons began again and the day wore on. Johnny did not pay much attention to his lessons. The thought of his mule lay heavy on his mind. What could he do with him?

When the bell rang for closing time, all the children rushed into the school yard and gathered around the mule. They were laughing and joking and poking fun at Johnny and his animal.

"Such a sad looking critter! What are you going to do with him, Johnny?" asked his little friend, Matthey.

Johnny did not feel very gay. "I don't know what to do with him," he said sadly. "If it took me two hours to get him a few blocks to school, how long will it take me to get him home? I

live five miles over the mountain. It will be black night before I could get him halfway there!"

Johnny leaned against the tree beside his mule and began to cry.

The children stopped laughing and looked soberly at each other.

"Hold on there, Johnny, you never can tell about a balking mule," comforted Matthey. "He may be ready to go by now. Maybe he'll start right off!"

Johnny brightened. He untied the mule's rope and tried to

233

lead him forward. But the mule was not ready to go and he did not start right off. Johnny braced himself and pulled. But the mule was not in the notion.

"Give me a hand-hold and I'll help you pull," said Matthey.

"I'll help too," said Nancy Belle. Both children threw their weight against the mule. But he did not budge. "Make room for us. We'll all pull!" said Hetty and Hank. They grabbed the mule's halter and hauled with all their might. But the mule only braced himself and stood in his tracks.

While the children were pulling and straining and puffing and blowing, the teacher came out of the schoolhouse. "Let me get a hold. I'll pull too!" she said. But one more made no difference to the mule. His mind was made up.

"My father once had a balking mule," piped up Nancy Belle, "and he used to get him to go by twisting his ear."

"Twisting his ear?" said Hezekiah. "Who ever heard of making a mule go by twisting his ear?"

"Well, it's true," declared the little girl. "That made him go."

"It wouldn't hurt to try it," said the teacher. "Go ahead, Nancy Belle, you are the one who knows how. You twist."

Nancy Belle grabbed the long droopy ear and twisted.

The mule stood pat.

"Twist again, twist again!" said the children, and Nancy twisted, but it was no good. The mule did not care to move, and twisting his ear did not make him change his mind. He only rolled his eyes and wiggled his ear to make sure that it was all in a piece.

"My uncle once had a balking mule," offered Hetty, "and he used to get behind him with a plank and push him."

"That's right," added Hank. "They used to push the mule a few steps forward and after that he would go all by himself."

"Maybe that's just what this mule needs," said Miss Mary. "Where can we find a plank?"

234

The children hustled around and underneath the edge of the schoolhouse, they found a long plank. They put it behind the mule and pushed. They huffed and they puffed, but the mule stood pat! They stopped for breath.

"Maybe the mule's hungry," spoke up Nancy Belle. "If we got a piece of corn and held it out to him, maybe he'd follow after it."

Johnny ran to the nearest house and brought back an ear of corn. He held it out to the mule. Yes, the mule was hungry. He stretched his neck toward the corn.

The children held their breath. The mule took one step forward. Johnny backed away, holding the corn just out of reach. The mule took another step forward, then another and another. A loud shout rose from the children.

"Hurrah! Hurrah! He's going!" they yelled.

What Will Pappy Think?

The teacher held the mule's halter while Johnny danced ahead with the corn. Through the town they went, clip, clop, clip-clop. Over the mountain trail they started as fast as they could go. But still Johnny did not seem very happy.

"A balking mule is no good to anybody," he moaned. "I'm afraid my Pappy will be as mad as fire when he sees this critter. Like as not, he'll give me a good licking."

"No use borrowing trouble," said the teacher. "Let's sing a song and forget about the mule."

Johnny struck up an old mountain hunting song and along they went singing.

After that Johnny felt better. "You can never tell," he said cheerfully, "maybe Pappy 'll be pleased to have a mule. He needs some kind of a critter to help him plow his potatoes. He has to do it now all by himself with an old hand plow."

"Why yes, of course," agreed the teacher. "It's likely that he'll be glad to get him."

"If only he wasn't a balker," said Johnny, wrinkling his forehead again. "Hardly anybody would want a balker."

"Oh, don't think about that," the teacher tried to cheer him up. "It's too beautiful on the mountains to get a head full of worry."

"Yes, it is pretty on the mountains." Johnny looked all around and forgot to worry about the mule. The air was full of the nice smell of pine, and the wildflowers were blooming everywhere.

But the mule did not care for anything except the ear of corn that was always just out of reach. He kept his eyes upon it and went clip-clopping along.

Johnny and the teacher felt cheerful until they came opposite Aunt Betsy's house.

Aunt Betsy was sitting on the porch busily spinning some wool to weave into a bedspread.

"My me! Whatever have you got there?" she cried when she saw Johnny and the teacher and the mule.

"It's a mule," Johnny replied. "I bought him at the auction for five cents."

"Five cents!" Aunt Betsy threw back her hands and laughed. Then she grew sober. "But he's not a balker, is he? I never heard of a mule's going for that little unless he was a balker."

"Yes'm," Johnny admitted uneasily. "He's a balker, all right."

"Oh my, my," Aunt Betsy shook her head. "I don't know what in the name of goodness you'll ever do with a balker."

After that there was hardly anything the teacher could say to comfort Johnny. They walked gloomily along.

A little farther along they came upon Uncle Boogermore Bennet sitting on his cabin steps, playing merrily on his old fiddle. "Land o' the livin'," he cried when he looked up and saw the mule. "You haven't got that old balking mule now, have you, Johnny?"

"Yes, sir, Uncle Boogermore," replied Johnny unhappily. "I bought him at the auction for five cents, and now I don't know what to do with him."

"Treat him like I do my wife when she gets a balky notion."

"How's that, Uncle Boogermore?" asked Johnny.

"Why I just leave her be until she gets a better one! Ha! Ha! Ha!" Uncle Boogermore laughed and slapped his leg as though he thought it a great joke.

On up the trail plodded Johnny feeling gloomier every minute. "The worst of it is, a mule has got a terrible appetite," he worried. "Why, that old mule could probably eat us out of house and home in no time. Miss Mary, I'm going to get that licking as sure as shooting. I wish I didn't have to go home at all."

But the mule took them there in a hurry.

Mammy and Pappy were waiting in front of the cabin looking down the road, wondering what kept Johnny so long.

When they saw him drawing the mule along, and the teacher holding the rope, their eyes popped open.

"Dog-gone my time!" exclaimed Pappy.

"What in the name of the land have you got there?" cried Mammy, laughing.

"It's a mule," replied Johnny nervously. "I bought him at the auction for five cents."

"For five cents! Then there must be something wrong with him," said Mammy.

"Yes'm, there is — a little something wrong. He's a balker, I reckon."

"A balking mule!" exclaimed Mammy. "Whatever could we do with a balking mule?"

"I—I—don't know, ma'am," stuttered Johnny, glancing at Pappy uneasily.

Pappy did not say anything at all. He just rubbed his chin and looked thoughtfully at the mule.

The sun was setting by this time. It was much too late for the teacher to return to town. She decided to spend the night with Johnny and his parents.

Mammy set a chicken on to cook in a big iron pot and later on they had supper—chicken-and-dumplings, hot corn bread and nice cold buttermilk. For dessert, there was honey from their own beehives and a pot full of hot tea.

It was a fine supper, but Johnny could not enjoy it. What was his Pappy thinking about that old balking mule? What was he going to do with him?

After the meal, everyone sat around the fire which leaped brightly in the old stone fire-place. Pappy got out his fiddle and played some merry tunes. Mammy sang some old mountain songs for the teacher.

Johnny sat in the chimney corner. He did not feel very happy because he kept wondering if his Pappy felt angry about the mule. At last he got up the courage to ask him.

"Pappy," he said timidly. "That balking mule is going to be sort of a nuisance, I reckon."

"Nuisance!" cried Pappy. "Why, I know how to make that old mule do all my plowing and hauling! Now you just wait and see."

He turned around and winked at Miss Mary. "Yes, siree! I know a little trick that will make a balking mule work harder than a honeybee!"

"What's that?" cried Johnny and Miss Mary in a breath.

"Wait until the morning," laughed Pappy. "Look out the window when you first wake up and you'll find out! Yes, siree, you'll find out!"

The teacher went to bed in the extra room, and Johnny climbed the ladder to his little room in the attic.

In the morning, he woke up early and looked out the window. There, pulling a plow briskly through the potato patch, was the balking mule. Hanging on to the handles of the plow was Pappy. He looked up and caught sight of Johnny.

"He's a fine, strong mule!" cried Pappy. "I'm much obliged to you!"

But the mule did not look up, nor to the right nor to the left. He was gazing greedily straight ahead at the ear of corn that was swinging on the end of a stick in front of his nose!

On Your Own

1. What worried Johnny most about having a balking mule?
   (a) Being late for school
   (b) How to get the mule home
   (c) What his father would say and do
   (d) How the children and grownups would tease him.

2. Who were the people who helped Johnny? What did they do? Why were they glad to help Johnny? How do you think Johnny felt about getting help? Why? How do you feel about having others help you?

3. What does each of these mountain expressions mean?
   (a) Stubborn as a mule
   (b) No use borrowing trouble
   (c) Work harder than a honeybee
   (d) Much obliged to you
   (e) A head full of worry
   (f) As mad as fire

MOON'S A–RISING

By ELLIS CREDLE

Moon's a-rising on Thunderhead Mountain,
Heigh! Heigh! Step and go lightly!
Hound dog's baying and we're a-going hunting,
Heigh! Heigh! Step and go lightly!

Chased a coon into a gum tree,
Heigh! Heigh! Step and go lightly!
Shot at the coon and hit a froggie.
Heigh! Heigh! Step and go lightly!

Thought I had a possum up in a tree there,
Heigh! Heigh! Step and go lightly!
Shook that tree and down come a he-bear!
Heigh! Heigh! Step and go lightly!

Oh, Mr. Bear, please don't ketch me, sir!
Heigh! Heigh! Step and go lightly!
Ketch that fellow behind the tree, sir!
Heigh! Heigh! Step and go lightly!

Moon's going down, my song is ended,
Heigh! Heigh! Step and go lightly!
Mighty good thing for I'm pretty nigh winded!
Heigh! Heigh! Step and go lightly!

Henry and Beezus

By Beverly Cleary

Life was certainly full of surprises for Henry Huggins. At the opening of the Colossal Market, things happened that were very funny to others, but not at all to him. It was his friend Beezus, short for Beatrice, who helped to get him out of trouble.

The Grand Opening

One Friday afternoon Henry and Ribsy, his dog, were walking home from school. They were going the long way past the Rose City Bike and Trike Shop so Henry could look at what he had come to think of as his bicycle—the one with the racy red frame and the built-in headlight. The only thing wrong with it was the price—fifty-nine dollars and ninety-five cents. It was exactly what Henry wanted, and he looked at it every time he had a chance.

After making sure his bike was still in the shop, Henry moved on. Across the street from the Supermarket he stopped to look at the new Colossal Market building that had just been finished. It covered a whole city block, and Henry had heard that the market would sell not only meats, groceries, and drugs, but would also have a filling station,

242

a soda fountain, a florist's stand, a beauty shop, a hardware store, and almost anything else you could think of.

Today there was a huge sign across the front of the building. Henry stopped to read it with mounting excitement.

Jeepers, thought Henry. That's a lot of free stuff. He decided to ask his mother and father to go. It was fun to collect free samples, and his mother might like a gardenia.

Henry and his mother and father joined the crowd of people visiting the new market that evening. His friend Beezus was with them, because her mother had to stay at home to put Ramona, the baby, to bed. Henry had given Ribsy a big bone for dinner so he would stay in his yard. If dogs had to stay out of the Supermarket, they would certainly have to stay out of the Colossal Market.

In front of the Colossal Market six searchlights sent giant fingers of light into the sky. Henry saw two of his friends,

When the girl handed her the flower, she took it, closed her eyes, and breathed deeply.

"Smell it, Henry," she said. "Did you ever smell anything so beautiful in your whole life?"

Henry gave it a quick sniff. "It's all right," he said, tying the string of his balloon to the button on his beanie. When he put the beanie back on his head, he hung onto it with one hand until he was sure the balloon wouldn't carry it away.

Free Samples

After agreeing to meet his mother and father by the front door at eight-thirty, Henry said, "Come on, Beezus, let's find some free samples."

Sniffing her gardenia, Beezus followed Henry, who had to stop before long and untangle his balloon string from the buttons of a lady's coat. Then they sampled doughnuts, hot from a doughnut machine, and looked over the largest selection of comic books they had ever seen. They tasted frozen orange juice

Robert and Scooter, talking to the men who ran the gasoline generators. As Henry and his father and mother and Beezus entered the market, someone handed each of them a ticket for the door prize. After they had written their names on the tickets and dropped them into a barrel, a girl in a fluffy blue skirt gave Mrs. Huggins a gardenia, while a clown offered Henry and Beezus balloons.

Beezus asked if she couldn't count as a lady and have a gardenia instead of a balloon.

and decided to pass up a free sample of dehydrated Vitaveg soup in order to watch a man demonstrate a gadget for making roses out of beets and turnips. Then they paused at the Colossal Beauty Shoppe to watch a lady have a free facial. Henry thought she looked funny with her hair wrapped in a towel and greasy stuff smeared on her face.

"Look!" Beezus grabbed Henry's arm and pointed to the platform where three girls from a dancing school had been tap-dancing. "The drawing for the door prizes is starting."

As the crowd pressed toward the platform, the master of ceremonies announced that the owner of the first ticket pulled from the barrel would receive, absolutely free of charge, one white side-wall tire from the Colossal Filling Station.

"Maybe you'll win it," said Beezus.

Henry wasn't sure his father needed one white side-wall tire, since all his other tires were black, so he wasn't disappointed when his name was not called. He soon lost interest in door prizes, because there were so many grownups in front of him that he couldn't see what was happening.

"Come on, Beezus," he said. "I bet this is a good time to get free samples."

They found Robert and Scooter in front of the doughnut machine. "This is my third free sample," said Scooter. "Come on, let's see what else we can find."

They tasted catsup, potato chips, jam, and cheese. Soon

245

the pockets of Henry's jeans bulged with sample boxes and bottles of Oatsies, Glit, and 3-Minit Whisk-it. Then they came to a display of Woofies Dog Food. The man standing behind the table handed the children pamphlets that explained how Woofies made dogs woof with joy, because it was made of lean red meat fortified with vitamins.

"Aren't you giving away samples?" asked Henry, thinking of Ribsy.

"No, I'm not," answered the man, and then added jokingly, "but I'll give you a can if you'll taste it."

"No, thanks," said Henry.

"Go on, taste it," said Robert.

"I bet you're scared to," scoffed Scooter.

"I'm not either," said Henry. "I just don't feel hungry."

"Ha." Scooter was scornful. "I dare you to eat it."

"Dares go first," said Henry.

"Only scaredy cats say that," answered Scooter.

Other boys and girls who were also collecting free samples

gathered to listen to the argument.

"Go on, eat it," someone said. "I bet it isn't so bad."

"Hey, gang!" a boy yelled. "He's going to eat dog food!"

"I am not," said Henry, but no one paid any attention. The Woofies man borrowed a can opener from another booth. Jeepers, thought Henry, how did I get into this mess?

The man clamped the opener onto the can. Henry looked around for a way out, but so many boys and girls were crowded around that he didn't see how he could escape. He wondered how Woofies tasted. Maybe it wasn't so bad. Ribsy ate it. If Henry really did eat it, he would be pointed out at school as the boy who ate dog food. Then he would be pretty important.

"Henry," whispered Beezus, "don't eat it."

Henry watched the can opener chew its way around the can. Ugh, he thought. He didn't want to be the boy who ate dog food, no matter how

much it impressed the kids. The man lifted the lid from the can, and Henry looked at the food made from lean red meat fortified with vitamins. At least it isn't raw, he thought, and wished something would happen.

What Next?

Something did happen.

The voice of the master of ceremonies blared out over the loud-speaker. "Henry Huggins!" The people around the platform laughed.

"Hey, that's me!" exclaimed Henry, bewildered. Why were all the people laughing?

"Will Mr. Huggins come to the platform to claim his prize?" asked the master of ceremonies.

Oh, thought Henry. The man meant his father. His father was Mr. Huggins, but it must be a mistake, because his father's first name wasn't Henry.

"Is Henry Huggins present?" asked the master of ceremonies.

"Henry, wake up," said Beezus. "You won a prize."

Henry looked at the can of dog food. "Here!" he yelled as loud as he could, and the crowd made way for him. Whew, that was close, he thought. He was so glad to get away from the Woofies, he didn't care what his prize was. Probably a basket of groceries.

As Henry climbed the steps to the platform, the audience howled with laughter. Henry looked around to see what was so funny, but he couldn't see anything to laugh at. Then he remembered the balloon tied to his beanie. Maybe that was it.

"So you are Henry Huggins!" boomed the master of ceremonies.

"Yes, sir," answered Henry, starting at the sound of his own voice over the loud-speaker. Why didn't people stop laughing? A balloon on a beanie wasn't that funny.

The master of ceremonies had an envelope in his hand. Henry, who was puzzled, looked inquiringly at him. What kind of a prize was it anyway? He had been so busy at the dog-food booth that he hadn't been listening.

"Henry Huggins, it gives me great pleasure to present you with fifty dollars' worth of work at the Colossal Market's own Beauty Shoppe!"

Henry's mouth dropped open and he felt his ears turn red. The crowd was a blur of pink faces in front of him, and laughter roared in his ears.

The master of ceremonies opened the envelope and took out some coupons. "Here are all the things this young man is entitled to. Two permanent waves, six special glamour haircuts, six Vita-Fluff shampoos, six waves, three facials, six manicures, and last but not least, one set of false eyelashes!"

248

Henry looked at the floor while the audience shrieked. Jeepers, he thought. Now he really was in trouble. The kids would never let him hear the last of this. Why couldn't he win a basket of groceries or a white side-wall tire like other people? He wished he had stayed and eaten the dog food.

"Well, young man," said the master of ceremonies, "don't you have anything to say?"

"Uh, thanks . . . I guess," said Henry, horrified at the way his voice roared over the loud-speaker.

The master of ceremonies pressed the envelope into Henry's hand, slapped him on the back, and boomed, "Good luck with your prize, young man!"

In Trouble

As Henry stumbled off the stage, Scooter got to him first. "When are you going to get your glamour haircut?" he demanded. "When are you getting false eye-lashes?"

"I bet . . ." Robert stopped to howl with laughter. "I bet you're going to be the prettiest boy at Glenwood School."

"Yoo-hoo, Henry!" yelled a couple of strange boys.

Scooter leaned against a shelf of canned goods and guffawed. "How are you going to wear your hair, Beautiful?"

Henry was sure his ears would burst into flames if they got any hotter. "You're not funny," he snapped.

"I know it," snorted Scooter. "I'm not half as funny as you're going to look with a glamour haircut and false eyelashes."

"I get it. Joke," said Henry coldly.

"Hi, Beautiful," called a strange boy. "How's the Vita-Fluff shampoo?"

"You're not so funny," said Henry.

"I bet you'll look real cute with a permanent wave," said another boy.

Henry glared and tried to move away, but there were too many people crowded around him. Jeepers, how was he ever going to get out of this?

"Say, it's the same boy who was going to eat Woofies," Henry heard someone say.

That gave Henry an idea. "Come on," he said. "Where's the Woofies man?"

"Are you really going to taste it?" Robert asked, as Henry passed him.

"Sure, I'm going to taste it," said Henry bravely. Anything to make people forget that prize,

he thought, as the boys and girls crowded after him.

"I didn't expect to see you again," said the Woofies man, holding out the can and a wooden spoon.

Henry dug the spoon into the dog food. Holding his breath, he popped a bite into his mouth and swallowed quickly. Why, it wasn't so bad. He hardly tasted it. He was pleased to see that all the boys and girls looked impressed.

"He really ate it," said Beezus, squirming through the crowd surrounding Henry. She still clutched her gardenia, which had turned brown from being sniffed so much.

Henry calmly took another bite, held his breath, and got it down. "M-m-m," he said. "It's lots better than K-9 Ration." And it was, too, because Ribsy preferred it.

There, thought Henry, that ought to make them forget the prize. Now if he could just get out of here before anyone mentioned it again.

"Here's your free sample."
The man handed Henry a can of
Woofies. "You earned it."

"Hey, Beautiful, how did it
taste?" asked Scooter.

Leave it to old Scooter,
thought Henry. Now he had
probably eaten the dog food for
nothing.

"Scooter McCarthy, you stop
teasing Henry," said Beezus.
"You're just jealous because you
didn't win something like Henry
did."

"Sure, you're jealous," said
Henry, but he didn't sound as if
he meant it.

"Joke," said Scooter.

Money, Money, Money

"Henry, aren't you thrilled?"
Beezus' eyes were shining.

Henry looked at her. Was
she crazy or something?

"I wish I'd won fifty dollars'
worth of work at the Colossal
Beauty Shoppe," she said enviously.

Well, what do you know! She
really means it, thought Henry.
These things were different with
girls. Why couldn't Beezus'
ticket have been pulled out of
the barrel instead of his?

"Henry, I have a dollar and
five cents at home," said Beezus.
"Will you sell me a wave coupon? I know waves cost more,
but that's all I have."

Until then Henry had not
really thought what he was going to do with the coupons. He
supposed he would have thrown
them away if there had been a
trash can handy. Maybe he
should just give Beezus the wave
coupon. Still, she was a sensi-
ble girl, and she had offered to
buy it. A dollar and five cents
would certainly come in handy.

251

"Sure, I'll sell it to you," said Henry, delighted with her offer.

"Thank you, Henry," said Beezus gratefully. "Now I can have my hair waved. I'm sure Mother won't mind just once for something special."

Then Henry saw his parents and Scooter's mother looking over the heads of the children.

"Come along, Henry and Beezus. We're leaving now," said Mr. Huggins. "Henry, you and your mother will have to get together about those coupons."

"Yes, Henry," said Mrs. Huggins, "I need a permanent. I'll give you the ten dollars and get it at the Colossal Beauty Shoppe. That would help your bike fund, wouldn't it?"

"Gee, Mom, would you?" Henry suddenly felt cheerful. Things weren't so bad after all.

Then Mrs. McCarthy said, "I don't need a permanent right now, but I will in a month or so. I'll give you ten dollars for the other permanent coupon." She opened her purse and took out a bill.

"Jeepers . . ." Henry was so pleased he couldn't think of anything to say.

"Hey, Mom," protested Scooter.

"What's the matter, Scooter?" asked his mother. "Don't you want me to help Henry?"

"Well . . . uh," said Scooter, "sure I do."

Hey, this is all right, thought Henry. Twenty-one dollars and five cents, just like that. And grownups didn't even think about teasing him. If only he could think of a way to sell the rest of the coupons.

Just then his mother said, "As soon as we get home, I'll phone your grandmother. I'm sure she'll be glad to buy some of your coupons."

"And what about his Aunt Doris?" suggested Mr. Huggins.

"Yes, and I can phone some of the girls in my bridge club," added Mrs. Huggins. She always called the ladies in her bridge club girls.

Henry could scarcely believe his luck. He didn't even have

to think of a way to sell his coupons. And only a few minutes ago he had been wishing he hadn't won them. Why, he might have thrown his riches away if Beezus hadn't offered to buy a wave coupon.

"I wish I'd won those coupons," said Robert. "You're sure lucky."

"I sure am," agreed Henry. Funny, nobody thought about teasing him now.

"Come on," said Mr. Huggins. "We don't want Beezus' mother to think we've lost her."

"There goes the boy who ate dog food," Henry heard someone whisper as he left the market.

The Bike

On the way home Mr. Huggins said to Henry, "Your bike fund is growing faster than you expected, isn't it, Beautiful?"

"Aw, Dad, cut it out." Henry pounded his father with his fist.

Everyone Mrs. Huggins spoke to agreed to buy some of Henry's beauty-shop coupons. By Saturday afternoon all the items were spoken for except one. No one wanted false eyelashes.

"Jeepers, Mom," said Henry, "that's almost fifty dollars in my bike fund, and my bike costs fifty-nine dollars and ninety-five cents. I'm almost there!"

"Have you picked out a bicycle already?" asked Mr. Huggins.

"I sure have, Dad. It's a beaut."

Mr. Huggins smiled. "In that case I think we can manage the ten dollars."

"Boy, oh boy! Mom, how soon do you think we can collect the money for the coupons?" Henry didn't see how he could wait another day. He was so close to that bicycle he could almost feel the handle grips in his hands and see the shiny new spokes twinkle as the wheels turned.

His father said, "How would you like me to lend you the money until next week?"

All Henry could say was, "Boy, oh boy!" as he ran into his room and snatched his genuine coonskin cap. Then he and his father and Ribsy drove to the Rose City Bike and Trike Shop.

Henry went straight to the bicycle with the racy red frame and the built-in headlight. "I'll take this one," he said.

"You're sure that's the right one?" asked his father.

"Yes, that's the one." Of course Henry was sure. Hadn't he gone out of his way to look at the bicycle at every possible chance for the last two weeks? Henry kept his hand on the bike until his father had written a check and the man had given him a receipt and a guarantee.

"It's all yours now," said his father.

"Gee . . ." Henry shoved up the parking stand and wheeled his bike out of the shop. His very own bicycle! He ran his fingers over the shiny frame and felt the leather on the seat. He turned on the built-in headlight and sounded the horn. Then he

"Would you, Dad?" asked Henry eagerly. "It's a lot of money."

Mr. Huggins rumpled Henry's hair. "Come on. Get your Daniel Boone hat and I'll take you down to the shop in the car. You can ride home on your new bike."

254

unsnapped his snap-on raccoon tail and fastened it to the handle bars. It was perfect.

Henry beamed at his father. "So long, Dad. See you at home." He threw his leg over the bike and rode off without wobbling once. Ribsy loped along beside him, and his father smiled and waved.

Henry turned down Klickitat Street so he could pass Scooter's house. When he saw Scooter sitting on his front steps folding *Journals,* he sounded his horn. He had waited a long time for this moment. "Hi, Scoot," he said casually, as he pedaled by with his spokes twinkling in the sunshine and his raccoon tail fluttering in the breeze.

On Your Own

1. Why do you think Henry ate the dog food?

2. Why did the people think it was so funny when he won the door prize? Make pictures to show how Henry felt at different times in the story.

3. What did the boys say when they teased Henry? What happened to cause them to suddenly stop teasing him and to think he was lucky?

4. Of all the people who helped Henry, which one do you think helped him most? Why do you think so?

5. Write a paragraph telling how you would use the money if you were to win a fifty-dollar door prize.

Thinking It Through

1. The boys in these stories had the problems listed below. Who had each of the problems? How was each problem solved?
   (a) How to get money for something he wanted very much to own
   (b) How to realize his wish for something he had not had in a long time
   (c) How to get his father to approve of something he was not sure his father would like

2. The stories and poems tell about other problems, such as daydreaming, wanting to have curly hair, being teased, making decisions. Do any of the stories or poems remind you of a problem of your own? Did the story or poem help you to solve your problem? How?

3. Each of the writers of these stories has her own way of telling a story, of showing how things happen, of making the characters seem real. Why are parts of the story about Denis so interesting? What makes you smile when you read the story about Johnny? Why is the story about Henry such a funny story? Why do you feel that you know the characters so well?

4. Which of the stories has its setting in a town? The mountains? The desert? Which story setting is most like yours? In which story setting would you like most to live? Why?

5. Each part of our country has music that helps to describe the land and people and tell what people do. Listen to records of mountain songs and of cowboy songs. You may know some of these already, and might enjoy singing them with others.

The Magic Carpet

Retold by GERTRUDE CHANDLER WARNER

People dreamed of flying thousands of years before they really flew. Do you think a trip on a flying carpet could be as beautiful and exciting as one in a jet?

Three Wonderful Things

Once there was a king who had three sons. One was named Houssain, one was named Ali, and the third one was named Ahmed. The king also had a niece who lived with them in the palace. Her own father and mother were dead. She was a very beautiful girl, and all three of the king's sons fell in love with her. They all wanted to marry her.

"But you cannot all marry Princess Light-of-Day," said the king to his sons. "The princess must choose the one she loves the best."

Now the princess could not tell which she loved the best. She said she loved them all.

One day the king sent for his three sons. He said to them, "If I gave the Princess Light-of-Day to one of you, the others would be angry. And so, my sons, I ask you each to go to a different country. Try to find something very strange and wonderful, such as I have never seen before. The one who brings me the most wonderful thing may marry the Princess Light-of-Day."

The three princes were willing to do this. Each one was sure that he would bring home the most wonderful thing.

The king gave each of them enough money to last a year. The three brothers dressed as merchants. The first day they traveled together and spent the first night at an inn. In the morning they parted. Each brother took a different road. They promised to come back to this same inn at the end of one year.

Prince Houssain traveled for many days to a great city. Merchants were selling all kinds of goods.

He soon found a room to live in. Then he spent his time looking over the things in the shops. The beautiful silks and velvets surprised him very much.

The prince walked so far along the streets that he was very tired. A merchant noticed that the prince walked slowly and looked tired. The merchant asked him to come in and rest. The prince thanked the merchant for his kindness and went in.

Just then another merchant went by the shop trying to sell a piece of carpet. He was asking forty bags of gold for it.

"Forty bags of gold!" cried the prince, going out. "The carpet is only six feet long."

Prince Houssain looked again at the carpet. It looked like any old carpet.

He said, "There must be something wonderful about this carpet that I cannot see."

"You are right again!" cried the merchant. "This is a magic carpet. When you sit on it and make a wish to go anywhere, the carpet will take you there instantly."

"If that is so, it is worth forty bags of gold," said Prince Houssain. "How do I know you are telling the truth?"

"I will let you try it," said the merchant. "Nothing could be fairer than that. You will soon see that I am right."

They put the carpet on the ground and both sat down on it. Prince Houssain said, "I wish to go to my room in this city."

Instantly the carpet rose into the air, and in a moment it set

them down in Prince Houssain's own room.

"Well, well! You did tell the truth," cried the prince. "I will buy the carpet and give you forty bags of gold and twenty gold pieces more for yourself. The carpet is the most strange and wonderful thing in the whole world."

Prince Houssain was sure now that he could marry the princess. His brothers could never find anything as wonderful as the carpet. He stayed a while longer for he was in no hurry to get to the inn.

All this time Prince Ali had been traveling with some jewel merchants. He talked so much about jewels that they thought he was a jewel merchant, too. And so they asked Prince Ali to stay with them.

The next morning, Prince Ali took a walk, looking at the wonderful jewels in the shops. He soon noticed a merchant going up and down the street with a small white tube in his hand.

"Forty bags of gold!" the merchant called.

Prince Ali went up to the merchant and said, "Are you out of your mind? Why do you ask forty bags of gold for that little tube?"

"You may well ask," said the merchant with a smile. "But this tube is really worth more than forty bags of gold."

"What is so wonderful about it?" asked the prince.

"Well, I will tell you," answered the merchant. "There is a glass inside the tube. When you look in the glass you can see anything you wish to see. Try it."

Prince Ali took the tube and wished to see his father, the king. He looked and saw his father in the palace, walking around and talking.

"This is wonderful!" cried the prince. "Now I wish to see the Princess Light-of-Day!" Instantly he could see her in the garden, laughing and talking with her ladies-in-waiting.

Prince Ali said, "Merchant, you are not out of your mind. That is a wonderful tube, and I will buy it. Come to my room, and I will give you forty bags of gold for it."

The prince took the merchant to his room. He counted out forty bags of gold and gave them to the merchant. The merchant gave him the tube.

Then Prince Ali was very happy indeed. He was sure that he could marry the princess. And so he started on his long journey back to the inn.

Prince Ahmed had also reached a big city. He walked around even longer than his brothers had done, looking at the beautiful things. He noticed a merchant who was calling out, "Forty bags of gold for this apple!"

The prince could see that it was not a real apple. He went up to the merchant and asked, "Why is that apple worth forty bags of gold?"

"Take it in your hand," said the merchant. "You see it is not a real apple? On the outside, it is not wonderful at all, but it will instantly make a sick person well. Even a dying person will be well the moment he smells this apple."

"Yes, yes!" shouted a man. "I have a very sick friend. I would buy the apple myself, but I do not have forty bags of gold."

"Take us to your friend," said Prince Ahmed.

The man showed them a house nearby. Inside there was a very sick man. Prince Ahmed could see that the sick man looked as if he might die at any moment.

"Smell this apple!" cried the merchant. And instantly the sick man became well and sat up.

"That is indeed very wonderful!" cried Prince Ahmed. "I want the apple. Here are forty bags of gold."

He could hardly wait to show the apple to his brothers. He was sure he had found the most wonderful thing in the world and would marry the princess. He took the apple and began his journey back to the inn. Prince Houssain and Prince Ali were already there.

Which One?

Prince Houssain, the oldest, began. "My brothers," he said, "Let us show our treasures to one another. Then we may know who will marry the princess. My treasure is the carpet I am sitting on. I gave forty bags of gold for it.

"No, it does not look wonderful, but it brought me here from a far country. It will take you wherever you wish to go. We can all go home on this magic carpet. Now, Ali and Ahmed, tell me if your treasures are more wonderful than this?"

"Well, I must say that your carpet is very strange and wonderful," said Prince Ali, the second son. "But I have something that is wonderful, too. Here is a small tube. I gave forty bags of gold for it, also. If you look through the glass in this end, you can see anything you wish to see. Take it, Brother Houssain. Try it."

Prince Houssain laughed and took the tube. "Let me see the Princess Light-of-Day!" he said. He put the tube up to his eye and looked into it. Then his brothers were frightened, for Prince Houssain cried out.

"The beautiful princess is very sick in bed! All her ladies-in-waiting are crying. She seems to be dying. All our wonderful treasures are no good if our beautiful princess dies. Take the tube, and see for yourselves."

Prince Ahmed looked quickly through the tube.

"Brothers," he said, "If we hurry, we may yet make her well. This magic apple is also

worth forty bags of gold. If the princess smells it, she will be well instantly. I have seen it tried, and it works."

"If that is so," said Prince Houssain, "we must go at once. Come, sit down on my magic carpet. There is room for us all."

The three brothers sat down on the carpet. It rose into the air and took them instantly to the bedroom of the Princess Light-of-Day.

The ladies-in-waiting were very much frightened by the three strange men coming in on a piece of carpet.

264

"Do not be afraid," said Prince Ahmed. "We have come to make the princess well."

"Oh, Prince! You cannot do that," said one of the women. "It is too late. The princess is going to die."

Prince Ahmed went to the side of the bed. He held out the magic apple. As soon as the princess smelled it, she sat up as if nothing had happened.

She looked around and saw the three brothers. She was very glad to see them and asked to be dressed at once.

While Princess Light-of-Day was dressing, the three brothers went to the king, who was waiting for them.

The three princes showed him their treasures and begged him to tell who could marry the princess. When the king saw the three treasures, he had nothing to say. He tried to think. He sat still and said nothing for a long time.

At last he said: "I would decide in favor of one of you, my sons, if I could only do so with justice. It is true that Prince Ahmed's apple saved the life of the princess; but consider whether the apple could have been of any service to her but for Prince Ali's tube which showed you all the danger she was in, and for Prince Houssain's carpet, which brought you all here in the nick of time. On the other hand, the tube would not have been of service without the carpet or the apple, nor the carpet without the apple and the tube. Therefore, not one of the three treasures is greater than another. I cannot decide the question; I must give you another test. You shall shoot an arrow, and I will bestow the princess upon him who shoots the farthest."

It was thus agreed, and Prince Houssain, as the oldest, bent his bow and shot his arrow. Prince Ali shot next, and his arrow was seen to fall a good way beyond his brother's. Prince Ahmed shot last of all, but although everyone searched for his arrow, it could not be found. The king therefore decided in favor of Prince Ahmed.

As for the beautiful Princess Light-of-Day, she had long ago decided that, since she had but one heart to give, she would bestow it upon Prince Ahmed. So they were married and lived together for the rest of their days in the greatest enjoyment and happiness.

On Your Own

1. Do you think the king made a just decision? Why? Below are listed three treasures of today. Which do you think is the most wonderful? Give reasons for your answer.

   (a) a wonder drug   (b) an airplane   (c) a TV

2. List the three treasures the brothers found. Beside each, list a treasure of today that is most like it.

3. How did each of these things make a difference in the story?
   (a) The king's feeling toward his sons
   (b) The willingness of the brothers to follow their father's decisions
   (c) The feeling the three brothers had for one another

4. Perhaps you would like to read other stories from the book *Arabian Nights*. You may also like to listen to music from a recording of *Scheherazade*. Scheherazade is supposed to have saved her own life by telling the tales known as *Arabian Nights*.

The Flight of Icarus

Retold by SALLY BENSON

Daedalus was a master engineer who invented wings of wax and feathers. This Greek myth is one of the earliest stories about men flying.

Once long ago in Greece there lived a famous builder named Daedalus. He went to visit Crete. King Minos, the ruler of the island, became angry with him, and ordered him shut up in a high tower that faced the lonely sea. In time, with the help of his young son, Icarus, Daedalus managed to escape from the tower, only to find himself a prisoner on the island. Several times he tried by bribery to stow away on one of the ships sailing from Crete, but King Minos kept watch over them and no ships were allowed to sail without being carefully searched.

Daedalus was an ingenious engineer and was not discouraged by his failures. "Minos may control the land and sea," he said, "but he does not control the air. I will try that way."

He called his son, Icarus, to him and told the boy to gather up all the feathers he could find on the rocky shore. As thousands of gulls soared over the island, Icarus soon collected a huge pile of feathers. Daedalus then melted some wax and made a frame in the shape of a bird's wing. The smallest feathers he pressed into the soft wax, and the large ones he tied on with thread. Icarus played about on the beach happily while his father worked, chasing the feathers that blew away in the strong wind that swept the island. Sometimes he took bits of wax and worked them into strange shapes with his fingers.

It was fun making the wings. The sun shone on the bright feathers; the breezes ruffled them. When they were finished, Daedalus fastened them to his shoulders and found himself lifted upwards, where he hung suspended in the air. Filled with excitement, he made another pair for his son. They were smaller than his own, but strong and beautiful.

Finally, one clear, wind-swept morning, the wings were finished, and Daedalus fastened them to his son's shoulders and taught him how to fly. He told him to watch the movements of the birds, how they soared and glided overhead. He pointed out the slow, graceful sweep of their wings as they beat the air steadily, without fluttering. Soon Icarus was sure that he, too, could fly, and raising his arms up and down, skirted over the white sand and even out over the waves, letting his feet touch the snowy foam as the water thundered and broke over the sharp rocks.

Daedalus watched him proudly but with misgivings. He called Icarus to his side, and putting his arm around the boy's shoulders, said, "Icarus, my son, we are about to make our flight. No human being has ever traveled through the air before, and I want you to listen carefully to my words. Keep at a moderate height, for if you fly too low, the fog and spray will burden your wings, and if you fly too high, the heat will melt the wax that holds them together. Keep near me and you will be safe."

He kissed Icarus and fastened the wings more tightly to his son's shoulders. Icarus, standing in the bright sun, the shining wings drooping gracefully from his shoulders, his golden hair wet with spray and his eyes bright and dark with excitement, looked like a lovely bird. Daedalus's eyes filled with tears, and turning away, he soared into the sky and called to Icarus to follow. From time to time, he looked back to see that the boy was safe and to note how he

managed his wings in his flight. As they flew across the land to test their powers before setting out across the dark, wild sea, plowmen below stopped their work and shepherds gazed in wonder, thinking Daedalus and Icarus were gods.

Father and son flew over Samos and Delos, which lay to their left, and Lebinthus, which lay on their right. Icarus, beating his wings in joy, felt the thrill of the cool wind on his face and the clear air above and below him. He flew higher and higher up into the blue sky until he

reached the clouds. His father saw him and called out in alarm. He tried to follow him, but he was heavier and his wings would not carry him.

Up and up Icarus soared, through the soft, misty clouds and out again toward the golden sun. He was bewitched by a sense of freedom and beat his wings frantically, so that they would carry him higher and higher to heaven itself. The blazing sun beat down on the wings and softened the wax.

Small feathers fell from the wings and floated softly down, warning Icarus to stay his flight and glide to earth. But the bewitched boy did not notice them until the sun became so hot that the largest feathers dropped off and he began to sink. Frantically he fluttered his arms, but no feathers remained to hold the air. He cried out to his father, but his voice was submerged in the blue waters of the sea, which has forever after been called by his name.

Daedalus, crazed by fear, called back to him, "Icarus! Icarus, my son, where are you?" At last he saw the feathers floating from the sky, and soon his son plunged through the clouds into the sea. Daedalus hurried to save him, but it was too late. He gathered the boy in his arms and flew to land, the tips of his wings dragging in the water from the double burden. Weeping bitterly, he buried his small son and called the land Icarus in his memory.

Then, with a flutter of wings, he once more took to the air, but the joy of his flight was gone, and his triumph over the air was bitter to him. He arrived safely in Sicily, where he built a temple to Apollo and hung up his wings of wax and feathers as an offering to the god.

On Your Own

1. A myth is an old, old story, partly true or not, which was used to explain something people could not understand. From what country did this myth come? Find the country on a map. Find Crete and Sicily also.

2. Why was Daedalus a prisoner? How did he try to escape?

3. What do the underlined words in these sentences mean?
   (a) He hung suspended in the air.
   (b) The water thundered over the sharp rocks.
   (c) They flew across the land to test their powers.
   (d) Thousands of gulls soared over the island.

4. What advice did his father give Icarus? Why did Icarus fail to follow it? Have you known anyone who had trouble because he acted like Icarus? Could this happen when one is riding on a bicycle or in a car, or flying in a plane? Compare the experience of Icarus with one you have had or know about.

WILBUR WRIGHT AND ORVILLE WRIGHT
1867–1912   1871–1948

By ROSEMARY AND STEPHEN VINCENT BENÉT

Said Orville Wright to Wilbur Wright,
"These birds are very trying.
I'm sick of hearing them cheep-cheep
About the fun of flying.
A bird has feathers, it is true.
That much I freely grant.
But, must that stop us, W?"
Said Wilbur Wright, "It shan't."

And so they built a glider, first,
And then they built another.
—There never were two brothers more
Devoted to each other.
They ran a dusty little shop
For bicycle-repairing,
And bought each other soda-pop
And praised each other's daring.

They glided here, they glided there,
They sometimes skinned their noses,
—For learning how to rule the air
Was not a bed of roses—
But each would murmur, afterward,
While patching up his bro,
"Are we discouraged, W?"
"Of course we are not, O!"

And finally, at Kitty Hawk
In Nineteen-Three (let's cheer it!),
The first real airplane really flew
With Orville there to steer it!
—And kingdoms may forget their kings
And dogs forget their bites,
But, not till Man forgets his wings,
Will men forget the Wrights.

MEASURE ME, SKY!

By Leonora Speyer

Measure me, sky!
    Tell me I reach by a song
Nearer the stars;
    I have been little so long.

Sky, be my depth,
    Wind, be my width and my height,
World, my heart's span;
    Loveliness, wings for my flight.

How Does It Feel on the Moon?

By ISAAC ASIMOV

Some day you may take a rocket ship to the moon.
What do you think you will find there?

Have you ever thought you might like to be on the moon? I'm sure you have seen pictures of the moon with its round craters. Perhaps you imagine yourself standing in one of them.

Of course, if you did, you might not really know it. The craters aren't as small as they seem in the photographs. Some of them are a hundred miles across. If you stood in the middle of one of these large ones, the round walls would be too far away to see.

It would take you hours to cross from one end of a large crater to the other in an automobile, if an ordinary automobile could run on the moon.

It can't, of course. An automobile must take in air to burn its gasoline just as a man must take in air to burn his food. The trouble is that there isn't any air at all on the moon.

For that reason, special rocket cars would have to be built to travel on the moon's surface. The rocket cars would carry

oxygen as well as the usual gasoline. On the earth, the oxygen is part of the air, but in rocket cars the oxygen would be made very cold and turned into a blue liquid. It would take up less room that way.

Any person on the moon would also have to carry his own air. He would wear a special moon suit carrying a supply of oxygen. This would be in a metal container strapped to the back and bits of oxygen would be allowed to escape into the suit so that the person could breathe.

The glass and metal of the moon suit would also protect

the person inside against radiation from the sun. On the earth, sunshine is warm and healthful, but that is because it passes through many miles of air before it reaches us. That part of sunlight which is too strong is filtered out. A bit does get through, however, and that is enough to give people with fair skins a sunburn on the beach.

Even on earth, a sunburn can hurt quite badly, but on the moon it would be much worse. There is no air to filter out the strong radiation and it is the suit that must keep it off.

The useful air, which we

breathe and which protects us from radiation, does something else, too. By means of its winds, it spreads the heat of sunshine evenly all over the earth so that it never gets too hot anywhere. On the moon, where there is no air, the sunshine in one spot can make it hot enough to boil water.

For that reason, a colony of Earthmen on the moon might have to dig caves under the ground where it would be always cool. If the caves could be made airtight and filled with air from the earth, men could even live there without wearing special moon suits.

They wouldn't have to stay in the caves all the time. They could put on their moon suits and come out when the sun was low in the sky. It would not be too hot then.

They might also come out at night, for there is both day and night on the moon. The moon's day and night are not quite like those of the earth, however. The moon turns much more slowly. It takes four weeks for the moon to turn around so that the day is two weeks long and so is the night.

In some ways, the nights would be far more beautiful than they are on the earth. The

277

stars would be the same ones we see from the earth, but they would be brighter. There is no air on the moon to take up some of the starlight and make the stars dim.

Besides, when the air moves on the earth, it makes the little star-beam shift to and fro, so that the star seems to twinkle. On the moon, there is none of this. The stars do not twinkle but are sharp steady little bits of bright light.

The daytime sky on the moon would be quite strange for it would not be blue. The blue of the earth's sky comes from bits

of sunlight that have been scattered and spread out by the dust in the air. That scattered light drowns out the stars.

On the moon, where there is no air, the daylight sky remains black. If you looked away from the sun, you would even see the stars.

The scattered light on the earth gets into the shadows which are really quite light for that reason. You can sit in the shadow of a building, for instance, and read a book easily. On the moon, where there is no air to scatter light, every shadow would be as black as pitch, even though there was sunshine a foot away.

Of course, on the moon, you could never see the moon in the sky. However, you could see something much more beautiful, something no one on the earth ever sees.

You could see the earth shining in the sky!

The earth would be much bigger than the moon we can see from here. It would be much brighter. However, it would seem to change shape as the moon does. It would be a "half-earth" sometimes, or just a narrow crescent—but a much larger one than the moon ever seems to turn into.

The clouds and air on the earth would make it look bluish-white as it shone in the sky. It would be hard to make out the shape of the continents.

But if you were on the moon, I think what you would notice most would be your feeling of lightness. The moon is much smaller than the earth so it can't pull down as hard. A boy weighing 60 pounds on the earth would weigh only 10 pounds on the moon.

Can you imagine how that would feel? If you jumped, you would fly high into the sky. You could break the high-jump and broad-jump records easily.

Of course, it might be hard to walk until you got used to the feeling of lightness. You wouldn't press as hard against the ground, so everything would seem very slippery and it would be easy to fall. Moon suits would have to come with heavy boots to hold you down.

The moon is a strange world. It would be hard to get there and hard to live there, but it will all be managed.

Three hundred years ago, men crossed a wide ocean to reach a New World here in America. That was hard, but it was done.

Now men look out across wide space to another New World. That will be reached too.

On Your Own

1. Suppose that you are on the moon.
    (a) How big are the moon's craters?
    (b) How do you travel?
    (c) What kind of space suit do you wear? Why?
    (d) Why is sunburn worse than on earth?
    (e) Where can you find a cool place to live?
    (f) How long is a day? A night?
    (g) Why are the nights so beautiful?
    (h) How does the daytime sky look?
    (i) How does the earth look?
    (j) Why is it hard to walk?
    (k) Do you weigh more or less than on earth? Why?
    (l) Describe the feeling of lightness.
    (m) Make a picture of an interesting sight on the moon.

2. If you are interested in space travel you will enjoy *You Will Go to the Moon* by Mae and Ira Freeman, and *Off Into Space!* by Margaret O. Hyde.

MOON–CRADLE

By PADRAIC COLUM

The moon-cradle's rocking and rocking,
Where a cloud and a cloud goes by:
Silently rocking and rocking,
The moon-cradle out in the sky.

NIGHT

By SARA TEASDALE

Stars over snow,
    And in the west a planet
Swinging below a star—
    Look for a lovely thing and you will find it,
It is not far—
    It never will be far.

281

Thinking It Through

1. Think about the three stories and answer these questions:
   (a) Which two stories could not have happened?
   (b) Which story is about something that may happen to you some day?

2. Pretend you were one of the following. Describe what you saw when you looked into the sky.
   (a) A shepherd when Icarus and Daedalus flew over
   (b) One of the ladies-in-waiting when three strange men came in on a piece of carpet

3. Have you ever listened to a count-down on TV? Describe the take-off of a rocket.

4. Make a picture time line of flight. You may begin far back in an imaginary past with the flying carpet and go on to the wings made for Icarus. Read the poem about the Wright brothers' flight. You may show their plane and date. In an encyclopedia look up *Lindbergh*. Show his plane with the date of his famous flight. Show a jet plane and a rocket ship for the present. If you want to go beyond the present, imagine a flying ship that might be and show it with an imaginary date.

THE WILDERNESS IS TAMED

By ELIZABETH COATSWORTH

The axe has cut the forest down,
The laboring ox has smoothed all clear,
Apples now grow where pine trees stood,
And slow cows graze instead of deer.

Where Indian fires once raised their smoke
The chimneys of a farmhouse stand,
And cocks crow barnyard challenges
To dawns that once saw savage land.

The axe, the plow, the binding wall,
By these the wilderness is tamed,
By these the white man's will is wrought,
The rivers bridged, the new towns named.

Little House on the Prairie

By LAURA INGALLS WILDER

Laura Ingalls Wilder wrote eight books, known as the "Little House" books, about her life in the early days of the West. The adventures begin in Wisconsin, where Laura was born in 1867, and *Little House in the Big Woods* tells the story. Then the family moved out to the wild Kansas country. Their trip and adventures are described in *Little House on the Prairie.*

In this story from *Little House on the Prairie,* Pa built a log cabin; Ma made it a home. But there were dangers on the prairie, as Laura and Mary found out.

THE HOUSE ON THE PRAIRIE

At last the family had reached the great prairie. Just before Laura went to sleep in the covered wagon, she heard Pa's fiddle music. The night was full of music and bright with stars.

Laura and Mary were up next morning earlier than the sun. They ate their breakfast of cornmeal mush with prairie hen gravy, and hurried to help Ma wash the dishes. Pa was loading everything else into the wagon and hitching up Pet and Patty.

When the sun rose, they were driving on across the prairie. There was no road now. Pet and Patty waded through the grasses, and the wagon left behind it only the tracks of its wheels.

Just before noon, Pa said, "Whoa!" The wagon stopped.

"Here we are, Caroline!" he said. "Right here we'll build our house."

Laura and Mary scrambled over the feedbox and dropped to the ground in a hurry. All around them there was nothing but grassy prairie spreading to the edge of the sky.

Quite near them, to the north, the creek bottoms lay below the prairie. Some darker green treetops showed, and beyond them bits of the rim of earthen bluffs held up the prairie's grasses. Far away to the east, a broken line of different greens lay on the prairie, and Pa said that was the river.

286

"That's the Verdigris River," he said, pointing it out to Ma.

Right away, he and Ma began to unload the wagon. They took out everything and piled it on the ground. Then they took off the wagon cover and put it over the pile. Then they took even the wagon box off, while Laura and Mary and Jack, the dog, watched.

The wagon had been home for a long time. Now there was nothing left of it but the four wheels and the parts that connected them. Pet and Patty were still hitched to the tongue. Pa took a bucket and his ax, and sitting on this skeleton wagon, he drove away. He drove right down into the prairie, out of sight.

"Where's Pa going?" Laura asked, and Ma said, "He's going to get a load of logs from the creek bottoms."

It was strange and frightening to be left without the wagon on the High Prairie. The land and the sky seemed too large, and Laura felt small. She wanted to hide and be still in

the tall grass, like a little prairie chicken. But she didn't. She helped Ma, while Mary sat on the grass and minded Baby Carrie.

First Laura and Ma made the beds, under the wagon cover tent. Then Ma arranged the boxes and bundles, while Laura pulled all the grass from a space in front of the tent. That made a bare place for the fire. They couldn't start the fire until Pa brought wood.

There was nothing more to do, so Laura explored a little. She did not go far from the tent.

But she found a queer little kind of tunnel in the grass. You'd never notice it if you looked across the waving grass-tops. But when you came to it, there it was—a narrow, straight, hard path down between the grass stems. It went out into the endless prairie.

Laura went along it a little way. She went slowly, and more slowly, and then she stood still and felt queer. So she turned around and came back quickly. When she looked over her shoulder, there wasn't anything there. But she hurried.

When Pa came riding back on a load of logs, Laura told him about that path. He said he had seen it yesterday. "It's some old trail," he said.

That night by the fire Laura asked again when she would see a papoose, but Pa didn't know. He said you never saw Indians unless they wanted you to see them. He had seen Indians when he was a boy in New York State, but Laura never had. She knew they were wild men with red skins, and their hatchets were called tomahawks.

Pa knew all about wild animals, so he must know about wild men, too. Laura thought he would show her a papoose some day, just as he had shown her fawns, and little bears, and wolves.

For days Pa hauled logs. He made two piles of them, one for the house and one for the stable. There began to be a road where he drove back and forth to the creek bottoms. And at night on their picket lines Pet and Patty ate the grass, till it was short and stubby all around the logpiles.

Pa began the house first. He paced off the size of it on the ground, then with his spade he dug a shallow little hollow along two sides of that space. Into these hollows he rolled two of the biggest logs. They were sound, strong logs, because they must hold up the house. They were called sills.

Then Pa chose two more strong, big logs, and he rolled these logs onto the ends of the sills, so that they made a hollow square. Now with his ax he cut a wide, deep notch near each end of these logs. He cut these notches out of the top of the log, but with his eye he measured the sills, and he cut the notches so that they would fit around half of the sill.

When the notches were cut, he rolled the log over. And the notches fitted down over the sill.

That finished the foundation of the house. It was one log high. The sills were half buried in the ground, and the logs on their ends fitted snugly to the ground. At the corners, where they crossed, the notches let them fit together so that they were no thicker than one log. And the two ends stuck out beyond the notches.

Next day Pa began the walls. From each side he rolled up a log, and he notched its ends so that it fitted down over the end logs. Then he rolled up logs from the ends, and notched them so that they fitted down over the side logs. Now the whole house was two logs high.

The logs fitted solidly together at the corners. But no log is ever perfectly straight, and all logs are bigger at one end, so cracks were left between them all along the walls. But that did not matter, because Pa would chink those cracks.

All by himself, he built the house three logs high. Then Ma helped him. Pa lifted one end of a log onto the wall, then Ma held it while he lifted the

other end. He stood up on the wall to cut the notches, and Ma helped roll and hold the log while he settled it where it should be to make the corner perfectly square.

So, log by log, they built the walls higher, till they were pretty high, and Laura couldn't get over them any more. She was tired of watching Pa and Ma build the house, and she went into the tall grass, exploring. Suddenly she heard Pa shout, "Let go! Get out from under!"

The big, heavy log was sliding. Pa was trying to hold up his end of it, to keep it from falling on Ma. He couldn't. It crashed down. Laura saw Ma huddled on the ground.

She got to Ma almost as quickly as Pa did. Pa knelt down and called Ma in a dreadful voice, and Ma gasped, "I'm all right."

The log was on her foot. Pa lifted the log and Ma pulled her foot from under it. Pa felt her to see if any bones were broken.

"Move your arms," he said. "Is your back hurt? Can you turn your head?" Ma moved her arms and turned her head.

"Thank God," Pa said. He helped Ma to sit up. She said again, "I'm all right, Charles. It's just my foot."

Quickly Pa took off her shoe and stocking. He felt her foot all over, moving the ankle and the instep and every toe. "Does it hurt much?" he asked.

Ma's face was gray and her mouth was a tight line. "Not much," she said.

"No bones broken," said Pa. "It's only a bad sprain."

Ma said, cheerfully: "Well, a sprain's soon mended. Don't be so upset, Charles."

"I blame myself," said Pa. "I should have used skids."

He helped Ma to the tent. He built up the fire and heated water. When the water was as hot as Ma could bear, she put her swollen foot into it.

It was providential that the foot was not crushed. Only a little hollow in the ground had saved it.

Pa kept pouring more hot water into the tub in which Ma's foot was soaking. Her foot was red from the heat and the puffed ankle began to turn purple. Ma took her foot out of the water and bound strips of rag tightly around and around the ankle. "I can manage," she said.

She could not get her shoe on. But she tied more rags around her foot, and she hobbled on it. She got supper as usual, only a little more slowly. But Pa said she could not help to build the house until her ankle was well.

He hewed out skids. These were long, flat slabs. One end rested on the ground, and the other end rested on the log wall. He was not going to lift any more logs; he and Ma would roll them up these skids.

But Ma's ankle was not well yet. When she unwrapped it in the evenings, to soak it in hot water, it was all purple and black and green and yellow. The house must wait.

Then one afternoon Pa came merrily whistling up the creek road. They had not expected him home from hunting so soon. As soon as he saw them he shouted, "Good news!"

They had a neighbor, only two miles away on the other side of the creek. Pa had met him in the woods. They were going to trade work and that would make it easier for everyone.

"He's a bachelor," said Pa, "and he says he can get along

without a house better than you and the girls can. So he's going to help me first. Then as soon as he gets his logs ready, I'll go over and help him."

They need not wait any longer for the house, and Ma need not do any more work on it.

"How do you like that, Caroline?" Pa asked, joyfully; and Ma said, "That's good, Charles. I'm glad."

Early next morning Mr. Edwards came. He was lean and tall and brown. He bowed to Ma and called her "Ma'am," politely. But he told Laura that he was a wildcat from Tennessee. He wore tall boots and a ragged jumper, and a coonskin cap, and he could spit tobacco juice farther than Laura had ever imagined that anyone could spit tobacco juice. He could hit anything he spit at, too. Laura tried and tried, but she could never spit so far or so well as Mr. Edwards could.

He was a fast worker. In one day he and Pa built those walls

as high as Pa wanted them. They joked and sang while they worked, and their axes made the chips fly.

On top of the walls they set up a skeleton roof of slender poles. Then in the south wall they cut a tall hole for a door, and in the west wall and the east wall they cut square holes for windows.

Laura couldn't wait to see the inside of the house. As soon as the tall hole was cut, she ran inside. Everything was striped there. Stripes of sunshine came through the cracks in the west wall, and stripes of shadow came down from the poles overhead. The stripes of shade and sunshine were all across Laura's hands and her arms and her bare feet. And through the cracks between the logs she could see stripes of prairie. The sweet smell of the prairie mixed with the sweet smell of cut wood.

Then, as Pa cut away the logs to make the window hole in the west wall, chunks of sunshine

Ma had cooked an especially good supper because they had company.

There was stewed jack rabbit with white flour dumplings and plenty of gravy. There was a steaming-hot, thick cornbread flavored with bacon fat. There was molasses to eat on the cornbread, but because this was a company supper they did not sweeten their coffee with molasses. Ma brought out the little paper sack of pale-brown store sugar.

Mr. Edwards said he surely did appreciate that supper.

Then Pa brought out his fiddle.

Mr. Edwards stretched out on the ground, to listen. But first Pa played for Laura and Mary. He played their very favorite song, and he sang it.

came in. When he finished, a big block of sunshine lay on the ground inside the house.

Around the door hole and the window holes, Pa and Mr. Edwards nailed thin slabs against the cut ends of the logs. And the house was finished, all but the roof. The walls were solid and the house was large, much larger than the tent. It was a nice house.

Mr. Edwards said he would go home now, but Pa and Ma said he must stay to supper.

Laura liked it best of all because Pa's voice went down deep, deep, deeper in that song.

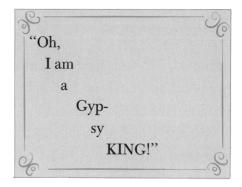

> "Oh, I am a Gypsy King!
> I come and go as I please!
> I pull my old nightcap down,
> And take the world at my ease."

Then his voice went deep, deep down, deeper than the very oldest bullfrog's.

> "Oh,
>   I am
>   a
>   Gyp-
>   sy
>   KING!"

They all laughed. Laura could hardly stop laughing.

"Oh, sing it again, Pa! Sing it again!" she cried, before she remembered that children must be seen and not heard. Then she was quiet.

Pa went on playing, and everything began to dance. Mr. Edwards rose up on one elbow, then he sat up, then he jumped up and he danced. He danced like a jumping jack in the moonlight, while Pa's fiddle kept on rollicking and his foot kept tapping the ground, and Laura's hands and Mary's hands were clapping together and their feet were patting, too.

"You're the fiddlin'est fool that ever I see!" Mr. Edwards shouted admiringly to Pa. He didn't stop dancing, Pa didn't stop playing. He played "Money Musk" and "Arkansas Traveler," "Irish Washerwoman" and the "Devil's Hornpipe."

Baby Carrie couldn't sleep in all that music. She sat up in Ma's lap, looking at Mr. Edwards with round eyes, and clapping her little hands and laughing.

Even the firelight danced, and all around its edge the shadows were dancing. Only the new house stood still and quiet in the dark, till the big moon rose and shone on its gray walls and the yellow chips around it.

Mr. Edwards said he must go. It was a long way back to his camp on the other side of the woods and the creek. He took his gun, and said good night to Laura and Mary and Ma. He said a bachelor got mighty lonesome, and he surely had enjoyed this evening of home life.

"Play, Ingalls!" he said. "Play me down the road!" So while he went down the creek road and out of sight, Pa played, and Pa and Mr. Edwards and Laura sang with all their might.

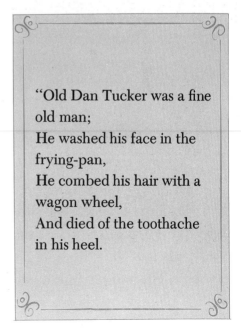

"Old Dan Tucker was a fine old man;
He washed his face in the frying-pan,
He combed his hair with a wagon wheel,
And died of the toothache in his heel.

> "Git out of the way for old
> Dan Tucker!
> He's too late to get his
> supper!
> Supper's over and the dishes
> washed,
> Nothing left but a piece of
> squash!
>
> "Old Dan Tucker went to
> town,
> Riding a mule, leading a
> houn' . . ."

Far over the prairie rang Pa's big voice and Laura's little one, and faintly from the creek bottoms came a last whoop from Mr. Edwards.

> "Git out of the way for old
> Dan Tucker!
> He's too late to get his
> supper!"

When Pa's fiddle stopped, they could not hear Mr. Edwards any more. Only the wind rustled in the prairie grasses. The big, yellow moon was sailing high overhead. The sky was so full of light that not one star twinkled in it, and all the prairie was a shadowy mellowness.

Then from the woods by the creek a nightingale began to sing.

Everything was silent, listening to the nightingale's song. The bird sang on and on. The cool wind moved over the prairie and the song was round and clear above the grasses' whispering. The sky was like a bowl of light overturned on the flat, black land.

The song ended. No one moved or spoke. Laura and Mary were quiet, Pa and Ma sat motionless. Only the wind stirred and the grasses sighed. Then Pa lifted the fiddle to his shoulder and softly touched the bow to the strings. A few notes fell like clear drops of water into the stillness. A pause, and Pa began to play the nightingale's song. The nightingale answered him. The nightingale began to sing again. It was singing with Pa's fiddle.

When the strings were silent, the nightingale went on singing. When it paused, the fiddle called to it and it sang again. The bird and the fiddle were talking to each other in the cool night under the moon.

Indians in the House

Pa had finished the house and built the stable. Laura lay in her little bed and watched the big, bright moon sailing in the sky. The family felt snug and safe inside the new home.

Early one morning Pa took his gun and went hunting.

He had meant to make the bedstead that day. He had brought in the slabs, when Ma said she had no meat for dinner. So he stood the slabs against the wall and took down his gun.

Jack, the dog, wanted to go hunting, too. His eyes begged Pa to take him, and whines came up from his chest and quivered in his throat till Laura almost cried with him. But Pa chained him to the stable.

"No, Jack," Pa said. "You must stay here and guard the place." Then he said to Mary and Laura, "Don't let him loose, girls."

Poor Jack lay down. It was a disgrace to be chained, and he felt it deeply. He turned his head from Pa and would not watch him going away with the gun on his shoulder. Pa went farther and farther away, till the prairies swallowed him and he was gone.

Laura tried to comfort Jack, but he would not be comforted. The more he thought about the chain, the worse he felt. Laura tried to cheer him up to frisk and play, but he only grew more sullen.

Both Mary and Laura felt that they could not leave Jack while he was so unhappy. So all that morning they stayed by the stable. They stroked Jack's smooth, brindled head and scratched around his ears, and told him how sorry they were that he must be chained. He lapped their hands a little bit, but he was very sad and angry.

297

His head was on Laura's knee and she was talking to him, when suddenly he stood up and growled a fierce, deep growl. The hair on his neck stood straight up and his eyes glared red.

Laura was frightened. Jack had never growled at her before. Then she looked over her shoulder, where Jack was looking, and she saw two naked wild men coming, one behind the other, on the Indian trail.

"Mary! Look!" she cried. Mary looked and saw them, too.

They were tall, thin, fierce-looking men. Their skin was brownish-red. Their heads seemed to go up to a peak, and the peak was a tuft of hair that stood straight up and ended in feathers. Their eyes were black and still and glittering, like snake's eyes.

They came closer and closer. Then they went out of sight, on the other side of the house.

Laura's head turned and so did Mary's, and they looked at the place where those terrible men would appear when they came past the house.

"Indians!" Mary whispered. Laura was shivery; there was a queer feeling in her middle and the bones in her legs felt weak.

She wanted to sit down. But she stood and looked and waited for those Indians to come out from beyond the house. The Indians did not do that.

All this time Jack had been growling. Now he stopped growling and was lunging against the chain. His eyes were red and his lips curled back and all the hair on his back was bristling. He bounded and bounded, clear off the ground, trying to get loose from the chain. Laura was glad that the chain kept him right there with her.

"Jack's here," she whispered to Mary. "Jack won't let them hurt us. We'll be safe if we stay close to Jack."

"They are in the house," Mary whispered. "They are in the house with Ma and Carrie."

Then Laura began to shake all over. She knew she must do something. She did not know what those Indians were doing to Ma and Baby Carrie. There was no sound at all from the house.

"Oh, what are they doing to Ma!" she screamed, in a whisper.

"Oh, I don't know!" Mary whispered.

"I'm going to let Jack loose," Laura whispered, hoarsely. "Jack will kill them."

"Pa said not to," Mary answered. They were too scared to speak out loud. They put their heads together and watched the house and whispered.

"He didn't know Indians would come," Laura said.

"He said not to let Jack loose." Mary was almost crying.

Laura thought of little Baby Carrie and Ma, shut in the house with those Indians. She said, "I'm going in to help Ma!"

She ran two steps, and walked a step, then she turned and flew back to Jack. She clutched him wildly and hung on to his strong, panting neck. Jack wouldn't let anything hurt her.

"We mustn't leave Ma in there alone," Mary whispered. She stood still and trembled.

She stumbled and fell down and her eyes popped open. She was up again and running before she could think. Mary was close behind her. They came to the door. It was open, and they slipped into the house without a sound.

The naked wild men stood by the fireplace. Ma was bending over the fire, cooking something. Carrie clung to Ma's skirts with both hands and her head was hidden in the folds.

Laura ran toward Ma, but just as she reached the hearth she smelled a horribly bad smell and she looked up at the Indians. Quick as a flash, she ducked behind the long, narrow slab that leaned against the wall.

The slab was just wide enough to cover both her eyes. If she held her head perfectly still and pressed her nose against the slab, she couldn't see the Indians. And she felt safer. But she couldn't help moving her head just a little, so that one eye peeped out and she could see the wild men.

Mary never could move when she was frightened.

Laura hid her face against Jack and held on to him tightly.

Then she made her arms let go. Her hands balled into fists and her eyes shut tight and she ran toward the house as fast as she could run.

First she saw their leather moccasins. Then their stringy, bare, red-brown legs, all the way up. Around their waists each of the Indians wore a leather thong, and the furry skin of a small animal hung down in front. The fur was striped black and white, and now Laura knew what made that smell. The skins were fresh skunk skins.

A knife like Pa's hunting knife, and a hatchet like Pa's hatchet, were stuck into each skunk skin.

The Indians' ribs made little ridges up their bare sides. Their arms were folded on their chests. At last Laura looked again at their faces and she dodged quickly behind the slab.

Their faces were bold and fierce and terrible. Their black eyes glittered. High on their foreheads and above their ears where hair grows, these wild men had no hair. But on top of their heads a tuft of hair stood straight up. It was wound around with string, and feathers were stuck in it.

When Laura peeked out from behind the slab again, both Indians were looking straight at her. Her heart jumped into her throat and choked her with its pounding. Two black eyes glittered down into her eyes. The Indian did not move, not one muscle of his face moved. Only his eyes shone and sparkled at her. Laura didn't move, either. She didn't even breathe.

The Indian made two short, harsh sounds in his throat. The other Indian made one sound like "Hah!" Laura hid her eyes behind the slab again.

She heard Ma take the cover off the bake-oven. She heard the Indians squat down on the hearth. After a while she heard them eating.

Laura peeked, and hid, and peeked again, while the Indians ate cornbread that Ma had baked. They ate every morsel of it, and even picked up the crumbs from the hearth. Ma stood and watched them and stroked Baby Carrie's head. Mary stood close behind Ma and held on to her sleeve.

Faintly Laura heard Jack's chain rattling. Jack was still trying to get loose.

When every crumb of the cornbread was gone, the Indians rose up. The skunk smell was stronger when they moved. One of them made harsh sounds in his throat again. Ma looked at him with big eyes; she did not say anything. The Indian turned around, the other Indian turned, too, and they walked across the floor and out through the door. Their feet made no sound at all.

Ma sighed a long, long sigh. She hugged Laura tight in one arm and Mary tight in the other arm, and through the window they watched those Indians going away, one behind the other, on the dim trail toward the west. Then Ma sat down on the bed and hugged Laura and Mary tighter, and trembled. She looked sick.

"Do you feel sick, Ma?" Mary asked her.

"No," said Ma. "I'm just thankful they're gone."

Laura wrinkled her nose and said, "They smell awful."

"That was the skunk skins they wore," Ma said.

Then they told her how they had left Jack and had come into the house because they were afraid the Indians would hurt her and Baby Carrie. Ma said they were her brave little girls.

"Now we must get dinner," she said. "Pa will be here soon and we must have dinner ready for him. Mary, bring me some wood. Laura, you may set the table."

Ma rolled up her sleeves and washed her hands and mixed cornbread, while Mary brought the wood and Laura set the table. She set a tin plate and knife and fork and cup for Pa, and the same for Ma, with Carrie's little tin cup beside Ma's. And she set tin plates and knives and forks for her and Mary, but only their one cup between the plates.

Ma made the cornmeal and water into two thin loaves, each shaped in a half circle. She laid the loaves with their straight sides together in the bake-oven, and she pressed her hand flat on top of each loaf. Pa always said he did not ask any other sweetening, when Ma put the prints of her hands on the loaves.

Laura had hardly set the table when Pa was there. He left a big rabbit and two prairie hens outside the door, and stepped in and laid his gun on its pegs. Laura and Mary ran and clutched him, both talking at once.

"What's all this? What's all this?" he said, rumpling their hair. "Indians? So you've seen Indians at last, have you, Laura?

I noticed they have a camp in a little valley west of here. Did Indians come to the house, Caroline?"

"Yes, Charles, two of them," Ma said. "I'm sorry, but they took all your tobacco, and they ate a lot of cornbread. They pointed to the cornmeal and made signs for me to cook some. I was afraid not to. Oh, Charles! I was afraid!"

"You did the right thing," Pa told her. "We don't want to make enemies of any Indians." Then he said, "Whew! What a smell."

"They wore fresh skunk skins," said Ma. "And that was all they wore."

"Must have been thick while they were here," Pa said.

"It was, Charles. We were short of cornmeal, too."

"Oh, well. We have enough to hold out awhile yet. And our meat is running all over the country. Don't worry, Caroline."

"But they took all your tobacco."

"Never mind," Pa said. "I'll get along without tobacco till I can make that trip to Independence. The main thing is to be on good terms with the Indians. We don't want to wake up some night with a band of the screeching dev—"

He stopped. Laura dreadfully wanted to know what he had been going to say. But Ma's lips were pressed together and she shook a little shake of her head at Pa.

"Come on, Mary and Laura!" Pa said. "We'll skin that rabbit and dress the prairie hens while that cornbread bakes. Hurry! I'm hungry as a wolf!"

They sat on the woodpile in the wind and sunshine and watched Pa work with his hunting knife. The big rabbit was shot through the eye, and the prairie hens' heads were shot clean away. They never knew what hit them, Pa said.

Laura held the edge of the rabbit skin while Pa's keen knife ripped it off the rabbit meat. "I'll salt this skin and peg it out on the house wall to dry," he said. "It will make a warm fur cap for some little girl to wear next winter."

But Laura could not forget the Indians. She said to Pa that if they had turned Jack loose, he would have eaten those Indians right up.

Pa laid down the knife. "Did you girls even think of turning Jack loose?" he asked, in a dreadful voice.

Laura's head bowed down and she whispered, "Yes, Pa."

"After I told you not to?" Pa said, in a more dreadful voice.

Laura couldn't speak, but Mary choked, "Yes, Pa."

For a moment Pa was silent. He sighed a long sigh like Ma's sigh after the Indians went away.

"After this," he said, in a terrible voice, "you girls remember always to do as you're told. Don't you even think of disobeying me. Do you hear?"

"Yes, Pa," Laura and Mary whispered.

"Do you know what would have happened if you had turned Jack loose?" Pa asked.

"No, Pa," they whispered.

"He would have bitten those Indians," said Pa. "Then there would have been trouble. Bad trouble. Do you understand?"

"Yes, Pa," they said. But they did not understand.

"Would they have killed Jack?" Laura asked.

"Yes. And that's not all. You girls remember this: you do as you're told, no matter what happens."

"Yes, Pa," Laura said, and Mary said, "Yes, Pa." They were glad they had not turned Jack loose.

"Do as you're told," said Pa, "and no harm will come to you."

. . . They were all happy that night. The fire on the hearth was pleasant, for on the High Prairie even the summer nights were cool. The red-checked cloth was on the table, the little china woman glimmered on the mantelshelf, and the new floor was golden in the flickering firelight. Outside, the night was large and full of stars. Pa sat for a long time in the doorway and played his fiddle and sang to Ma and Mary and Laura in the house and to the starry night outside.

IN MY MOTHER'S HOUSE

By ANN NOLAN CLARK

This is my Mother's house;
My Father made it.
He made it with adobe bricks;
He made it strong;

He made it big;
He made it high;
My Mother's house,
I live in it.

In my Mother's house
There is a fireplace:
The fireplace holds the fire.
On dark nights the fire is bright;
On cold nights the fire is warm.
The fire is always there,
To help me see,
To keep me warm.

Thinking It Through

1. The "Little House" books have been favorites of boys and girls for many years.

   (a) A story may be a favorite because of what it is about. As in all the books, this story from *Little House on the Prairie* tells of hardships, yet of fun and love and excitement, too. There is Ma's good cooking, Pa's music, and the warm, safe feeling of home. Does the story make you think of some things in your own life?

   (b) A story may be interesting because of the style, or the way it is told. A good author uses words well. What words does the writer use to help you to see the wide prairie, hear Pa's singing and his fiddle, feel frightened at times and safe at others?

   (c) A story may be enjoyed because of the plot, or the things that happen. When did you first begin to feel that Laura might see some Indians? What are some things about the plot that make you like the story?

   (d) A story may be liked because the characters seem like real people. The writer does not say that Ma was brave, but you know Ma is by the way she says things such as, "I can manage." Which parts tell you that Pa was strong and liked to do a good job? How do you know Laura so well?

2. Why do you think the "Little House" books are favorites of boys and girls? Is it because of what the stories are about, the plot, the style, the characters, or all of these? What do you like most about the story you have just read from *Little House on the Prairie?*

Glossary

This glossary contains the more unusual or difficult words in *Peacock Lane*.

The pronunciation of each word is given between slanting lines. Before a syllable with strong stress, a high mark (') is placed; before a syllable with medium stress, a low mark (ˌ) is placed; before a syllable with weak stress, no mark at all is placed; as in **penmanship** \ˈpen-mən-ˌship\.

Each definition of a word is followed by a number. The number refers to the page on which the word is first used with that particular meaning.

The key below will help you to pronounce the words.

a	m**a**t, m**a**p		ō	b**o**ne, sn**ow**
ā	**a**ge, v**ei**n		ȯ	c**o**rn, s**aw**, **a**ll
ä	c**o**t, b**o**ther		ȯi	c**oi**n, b**oy**
à	c**a**rt, f**a**ther			
aů	s**ou**nd, n**ow**			
			th	**th**in, e**th**er
			<u>th</u>	**th**en, ei**th**er
e	b**e**t, b**e**d			
ē	**e**venl**y**, b**ea**t, sl**ee**p**y**		ü	r**u**le, f**oo**l
			ů	p**u**ll, w**oo**d
i	t**i**p, **i**nvent			
ī	s**i**de, b**uy**		zh	vi**s**ion

ə	b**a**nan**a**	s**i**lent	cap**i**tal	c**o**llect	s**u**ppose
	perplex	s**e**rpent	col**o**r	s**u**pper	p**u**rple

The system of indicating pronunciation shown above is used by permission, from *Webster's Elementary Dictionary*, copyright 1961 by G. & C. Merriam Company, publishers of the Merriam-Webster dictionaries.

A

advice \əd-ˈvīs\ A suggestion about what one should do. (105)

almond eyes \ˈäm-ənd ˈīz\ Eyes with a three-cornered shape, as in the almond nut. (62)

antelope \ˈant-l-ˌōp\ A deerlike animal with long horns. (49)

appreciate \ə-ˈprē-shē-ˌāt\ To enjoy; to be grateful for. (293)

approval \ə-ˈprüv-l\ Thinking well of a person or thing. (96)

308

atomic engine \ ə-'täm-ik 'enj-n \ In a submarine, an engine with flat blades which are turned by the force of the steam made by moving liquids through pipes near a piece of uranium. (202)

atomic power \ ə-'täm-ik 'paùr \ Power inside the tiny particles, or atoms, that make up all matter, and which can sometimes be used for running engines. (202)

auction sale \ 'öksh-n 'sāl \ A public sale in which things are sold to the persons who offer the most money for them. (232)

axle \ 'aks-l \ The rod on which a wheel turns. (105)

B

bachelor \ 'bach-lər \ A man who has not married. (291)

balance scale \ 'bal-əns 'skāl \ A machine for weighing, having two pans or trays: one to hold an object of known weight and the other to hold an object to be weighed. (92)

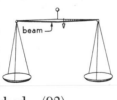

balcony \ 'balk-n-ē \ A platform enclosed by a low wall or a railing, built out from the side of a building. (144)

bamboo \ bam-'bü \ A tall, treelike plant with stiff, hollow, thick-jointed stems. (82)

base \ 'bās \ The part on which something rests; the bottom. (86)

beam \ 'bēm \ The crossbar of a balance from the ends of which scales or weights hang. (95)

beckoned \ 'bek-nd \ Called a person by moving the hand or head. (113)

bestow \ bē-'stō \ To give. (266)

bewildered \ bē-'wild-rd \ Confused; filled with uncertainty. (247)

bid \ 'bid \ Offered; an offer, such as one makes at an auction. (232)

birds of paradise \ 'bərdz əv 'par-ə-ˌdīs \ Brightly colored birds with long feathers. (196)

bleached \ 'blēcht \ Whitened. (221)

bluffs \ 'bləfs \ High, steep banks or cliffs. (286)

blunt snout \ 'blənt 'snaùt \ The thick, rounded nose of an animal. (52)

boasted \ 'bōst-əd \ Praised himself; bragged. (82)

bribery \ 'brīb-r-ē \ Offering a person something he wants so that he will do something wrong. (267)

brim \ 'brim \ The edge. (181)

brindled \ 'brind-ld \ Gray or tan with darker streaks or spots. (297)

broad \ 'bròd \ Open; full. (175)

budge \ 'bəj \ To move. (169)

burnished \ 'bər-nisht \ Polished. (116)

burros \ 'bər-ōz \ Small donkeys used as pack animals. (174)

C

cactus \ 'kak-təs \ A kind of prickly plant. (14)

canvas \ 'kan-vəs \ A very strong cloth, usually of cotton. (81)

Cape Horn\ 'kāp 'hȯrn\ A point of land at the southern tip of South America. (69)

carburetor \ 'kȧrb-r͵āt-r\ That part of a motor or engine in which liquid fuel, such as gasoline, is mixed with air to make it ready to be exploded. (202)

cat's-claw \ 'kats-͵klȯ\ A prickly shrub. (14)

channel\ 'chan-l\ A narrow body of water deep enough to allow a ship to pass through. (193)

chaps \ 'shaps\ Leather leggings worn by cowboys. (15)

chimney sweep\ 'chim-nē ͵swēp\ A person whose work is cleaning out chimneys. (171)

chink\ 'chingk\ To fill up cracks in walls. (289)

chrysanthemums \ kri-'santh-ə-məmz\ Round flowers that have many petals and that bloom in the fall. (135)

cicadas \ sə-'kād-əz\ Large insects with wings that can be seen through; locusts. (82)

clematis \ 'klem-ə-təs\ A vine with bunches of sweet-smelling white or purple flowers. (162)

cockchafer \ 'käk-͵chā-fər\ A large beetle. (30)

cocoons \ kə-'künz\ Silky cases in which caterpillars live while they are turning into butterflies or moths. (135)

colleagues\ 'käl-͵ēgz\ Fellow workers. (92)

colony\ 'käl-ə-nē\ A group of people who settle in a new country but who stay citizens of the country where they were born. (277)

comet\ 'käm-ət\ A heavenly body with a starlike point and often with a tail of light. (77)

congratulate \ kən-'grach-l-͵āt\ To tell a person that one is happy about his success. (60)

continent \ 'känt-n-ənt\ One of the six large masses of land on the earth: North America, South America, Europe, Asia, Africa, and Australia. (189)

convert \ kən-'vərt\ To cause a person to believe in God or to change his religion. (192)

courtier \ 'kȯrt-ē-ər\ A person who lives at the court of a ruler. (105)

craters\ 'krāt-rz\ Bowl-shaped holes on the moon's surface, ranging in size from fairly small holes to huge ones many miles across. (275)

crescent \ 'kres-nt \ The shape of the new moon. (279)

cruise\ 'krüz\ A trip made by a ship that is sailing from place to place. (201)

cultivating\ 'kəl-tə-͵vāt-ing\ Helping plants to grow by loosening the earth around them or by treating them carefully. (81)

current\ 'kər-ənt\ Water that flows in one direction. (70)

curtsy \ 'kərt-sē \ A ladylike bow. (28)

D

deal \ 'dēl \ Amount. (48)

decision \ dē-'sizh-n \ 1. A judgment. (110) 2. A choice. (256)

dehydrated \ dē-'hīd-ˌrāt-əd \ With water taken from; dried. (245)

delicate \ 'del-ik-ət \ Thin. (134)

delicious \ dē-'lish-əs \ Delightful, especially to taste or smell. (65)

de luxe \ də 'ləks \ Very grand. (243)

demonstrate \ 'dem-ən-ˌstrāt \ To show publicly. (245)

depth \ 'depth \ Deepness; distance down; distance through. (96)

deserted \ dē-'zərt-əd \ Left without orders, not intending to return. (194)

desperately \ 'desp-rət-lē \ Almost beyond hope. (180)

determined \ dē-'tər-mənd \ With one's mind firmly made up. (191)

diary \ 'dīr-ē \ An account, written down each day, of what has happened or what one has done or thought. (208)

diesel engines \ 'dē-zəl 'enj-nz \ Engines in which the fuel and air are squeezed into such a small space that an explosion is caused without a spark. (202)

dignity \ 'dig-nət-ē \ The manner that comes from thinking well of one's self and having the respect of others. (136)

dik-dik \ 'dik-ˌdik \ An antelope about as big as a large rabbit. (48)

disfigured \ dis-'fig-yərd \ Made less beautiful or less perfect. (37)

disgraceful \ dis-'grās-fl \ Shameful. (35)

dismounted \ dis-'maunt-əd \ Got down from. (181)

disobedient \ dis-ə-'bēd-ē-ənt \ Refusing or failing to do what one has been ordered to do. (166)

distant \ 'dis-tənt \ Far away. (62)

dragonflies \ 'drag-n-ˌflīz \ Large insects with long bodies and two pairs of wings. (82)

dramatized \ 'dram-ə-ˌtīzd \ Made into a play. (122)

drive \ 'drīv \ A great many logs floating together down the river. (41)

E

embroidered \ im-'broid-rd \ Sewed designs with fancy stitches. (134)

enlist \ in-'list \ To join. (207)

enormous \ ē-'nor-məs \ Huge. (37)

enviously \ 'en-vē-əs-lē \ Discontentedly, because of another's good fortune, and because one wants to have the same good fortune. (251)

Equator \ ē-'kwāt-r \ An imaginary line around the middle of the earth, exactly halfway between the North Pole and the South Pole. (70)

explorer \ iks-'plor-r \ One who searches or travels for purposes of discovery. (188)

expression \ iks-'presh-n \ A look on the face that shows feeling. (51)

extraordinary \ eks-'trord-n-ˌer-ē \ Unusual; remarkable. (36)

F

fabulous \ 'fab-yə-ləs \ Wonderful; like a fable. (188)

fading \ 'fād-ing \ Becoming small and dim. (190)

familiar \ fə-'mil-yər \ Known to all. (113)

fangs \ 'fangz \ Long, sharp teeth of animals. (29)

fashioned \ 'fash-nd \ Made, built, shaped. (86)

fault \ 'folt \ A weakness in character. (37)

fertilizer \ 'fərt-l-ˌīz-r \ Anything spread on the earth so that plants will be healthy. (83)

fetch \ 'fech \ To go, get, and bring back. (106)

fiber \ 'fib-r \ A tough substance with thread-like parts. (136)

filtered \ 'filt-rd \ Passed through air and becoming less strong. (276)

fin \ 'fin \ One of the thin, paddle-like parts on the back, tail, and sides of a fish, used to steer and to balance its body. (71)

flagship \ 'flag-ˌship \ The ship which carries the commander of a group of ships and which flies his flag. (190)

flattery \ 'flat-r-ē \ Praise that is not the truth, or praise beyond the truth. (120)

fleet \ 'flēt \ A group of ships under one captain. (188)

flint \ 'flint \ A piece of very hard stone used to strike fire with steel. (151)

florist's stand \ 'flōr-əsts 'stand \ A place where flowers are sold. (243)

fortified \ 'fort-ə-ˌfīd \ Made strong; strengthened. (246)

fragrance \ 'frāg-rəns \ A sweet or pleasing smell. (63)

fuel \ 'fyü-əl \ Anything, such as coal, wood, or gasoline, that can be burned up to make heat or power. (202)

G

gangplank \ 'gang-ˌplangk \ A movable bridge used in passing on and off a ship. (94)

gazelle \ gə-'zel \ A small antelope known for its grace, swiftness, and large, soft eyes. (48)

generators \ 'jen-r-ˌāt-rz \ Machines that produce electric current. (244)

Genoese \ 'jen-ə-ˌwēz \ From Genoa, Italy, the capital of an independent Italian republic in the time of Columbus. (189)

giraffe \ jə-'raf \ A spotted animal, about eighteen feet tall, with long legs and a very long neck. (48)

glamour \ 'glam-r \ Exciting; glorified. (248)

goblin \ 'gäb-lən \ An ugly creature with evil or playful ways. (164)

Guam \ 'gwäm \ Largest and southernmost of the Mariana Islands in the western Pacific Ocean. (206)

guarantee \ ˌgar-ən-'tē \ A printed slip giving a promise to replace goods if they are not as represented. (254)

guffawed \ gə-'fȯd \ Laughed loudly. (249)

Gulf of Mexico \ 'gəlf əv 'mek-si-kō \ A large body of water partly enclosed by land, south of the United States. (68)

Gulf Stream \ 'gəlf 'strēm \ Warm ocean water flowing from the Gulf of Mexico to the British Isles. (68)

H

hardware \ 'härd-ˌwer \ Things made of metal, such as locks, knives, nails, tools. (27)

harness \ 'här-nəs \ The whole set of leather straps used to ride or steer an animal, or to fasten him to a plow or wagon. (41)

hartebeest \ 'här-tə-bēst \ A large, horned, swift-footed antelope. (48)

hatch \ 'hach \ An opening in the deck of a ship. (205)

hearth \ 'härth \ The floor of a fireplace. (300)

heathen festival \ 'hē<u>th</u>-n 'fes-təv-l \ A time of merrymaking for people who do not know about or believe in the God of the Bible. (160)

heedlessly \ 'hēd-ləs-lē \ Carelessly. (29)

hewed \ 'hyüd \ Shaped with an ax. (291)

horizon \ hə-'rīz-n \ The line where the earth and sky seem to meet. (100)

human being \ 'hyü-mən 'bē-ing \ A living person. (269)

hyena \ hī-'ē-nə \ A wild, meat-eating animal about the size of a large dog. (50)

I

indignantly \ in-'dig-nənt-lē \ Angrily, because of unfair treatment. (27)

instance \ 'ins-təns \ An example. (278)

instant \ 'ins-tənt \ A moment. (152)

instep \ 'in-ˌstep \ The top of a person's foot between the toes and the ankle. (290)

International Date Line \ ˌint-r-'nash-n-əl 'dāt 'līn \ An imaginary line which marks the spot on the earth's surface where each new calendar day begins. (209)

J

jack rabbit \ 'jak ˌrab-ət \ A large hare of western North America, having very long back legs and ears. (217)

jet \ 'jet \ 1. A hard, black, shiny mineral, used for beads and buttons. (116) 2. An airplane with an engine in which the burning fuel makes a stream of heated air and gases which is forced out at the back of the plane, thus moving it forward. (258)

jumper \ 'jəmp-r \ A loose blouse or jacket sometimes worn by workmen. (292)

K

knapsack\\'nap-ˌsak\\A case of canvas or leather carried on the back. (145)

L

Ladrones \\lə-'drōnz\\ A group of islands, now called the Marianas, in the western Pacific Ocean. (194)

landmarks\\'land-ˌmȧrks\\Objects on land that can be easily seen and used as a guide by those who sail the sea. (206)

leagues\\'lēgz\\Measures of distance, each one about three miles. (76)

lingering\\'ling-gr-ing\\Staying on; putting off leaving. (112)

Lisbon\\'liz-bən\\The capital city of Portugal. (188)

loom \\'lüm\\ A frame for weaving cloth. (137)

lotus\\'lōt-əs\\A kind of water lily with large, round leaves and pink or yellow flowers. (132)

lumbered\\'ləm-brd\\Moved along heavily and noisily. (94)

lumberjack\\'ləm-br-jak\\A man who cuts down trees and makes logs. (40)

lunging\\'lənj-ing\\Making a sudden leap forward. (299)

M

maze\\'māz\\A network of passages through which it is hard to find one's way. (194)

mellowness \\'mel-ō-nəs\\ Softness; richness. (296)

mesquite\\məs-'kēt\\A spiny deep-rooted tree or shrub of the southwestern United States that has pods which are used as livestock feed. (14)

Mexico\\'mek-si-kō\\A country in North America, south of the United States. (174)

millstones\\'mil-ˌstōnz\\Two round, flat stones for grinding corn and other grain. (147)

ministers\\'min-əst-rz\\A group of men who help the ruler to govern the country. (133)

molasses\\mə-'las-əz\\A thick, sweet, brown liquid obtained when sugar is made. (42)

morsel\\'mȯrs-l\\A small bit of food. (301)

moths \\'mȯthz \\ Broad-winged insects, something like butterflies, that fly at night. (87)

mulberry tree \\'məl-ˌber-ē 'trē\\ A tree with sweet berries whose leaves are used to feed silkworms. (132)

mush\\'məsh\\Cornmeal boiled in water. (161)

mutiny\\'myüt-nē\\The refusal of the sailors to obey their captain. (193)

myth\\'mith\\A legend or story used to explain something that man could not understand. (267)

N

natives\\'nāt-ivz\\People belonging to a certain country because they were born there. (191)

nautical miles \ 'nȯt-ik-l 'mīlz \ Measures of distance used in sailing a ship or flying a plane; each about 6076 feet. (209)

navigation \ ,nav-ə-'gāsh-n \ The science of finding in what direction a ship should sail in order to reach a certain spot. (189)

nick of time \ 'nik əv 'tīm \ The right moment exactly. (265)

nightingale \ 'nīt-n-,gāl \ A reddish-brown bird, famous for its beautiful song. (296)

nimble \ 'nim-bl \ Quick-moving. (103)

notch \ 'näch \ A V-shaped cut in an edge or surface. (288)

notions \ 'nōsh-nz \ Small, useful articles, such as pins and needles. (27)

O

obliged \ ə-'blījd \ 1. Forced. (150) 2. Owing thanks. (240)

orneriest \ 'ȯr-nər-ē-əst \ The most short-tempered. (74)

oxygen \ 'äks-ij-n \ A gas without color or smell that forms about one-fifth of the air. (203)

P

paddies \ 'pa-dēz \ Wet fields used for growing rice. (80)

paloverde tree \ ,pa-lō-'vərd-ē 'trē \ A thorny tree with smooth, light-green bark and bright yellow flowers. (221)

pamphlets \ 'pam-fləts \ Booklets in paper covers. (246)

Panama Canal \ 'pan-ə-,mȯ kə-'nal \ A waterway built through the narrowest part of Central America so that ships will not have to sail around Cape Horn. (98)

partridge \ 'pär-trij \ A large, wild henlike bird often hunted and eaten. (64)

paused \ 'pȯzd \ Stopped for a time; waited. (245)

peacock \ 'pē-,käk \ A large bird with a colorful tail which can be spread out like a fan. (138)

peanut brittle \ 'pē-nət 'brit-l \ A hard, flat candy made of peanuts and molasses. (44)

peasant \ 'pez-nt \ A person who owns or works on a small farm. (100)

pell-mell \ 'pel-'mel \ In a great hurry. (52)

periscope \ 'per-ə-,skōp \ A tube with mirrors fixed inside it so that a person at the bottom end of the tube sees what is reflected in the topmost mirror. (205)

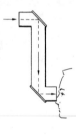

permanent \ 'pər-mə-nənt \ A long-lasting curling of the hair. (252)

pewter \ 'pyüt-r \ A mixture of tin with lead, copper, or other metals, which is used to make dishes. (162)

Philippine Islands \ 'fil-ə-,pēn ,ī-ləndz \ A group of 7100 islands in the western Pacific Ocean. (206)

picked \ 'pikt \ Played a stringed instrument with the fingers. (133)

picketed \ 'pik-ət-əd \ Tied. (168)

pier \ 'pir \ A landing place for ships which is built out over the water and held up by thick posts. (188)

planks \ 'plangks \ Long, flat, thick boards. (41)

pleaded \ 'plēd-əd \ Argued; begged. (113)

plod \ 'pläd \ To walk slowly, steadily, and heavily. (100)

Portuguese \ 'pōr-chə-gēz \ Of Portugal. (188)

prairie \ 'prer-ē \ A large piece of level or rolling land with grass but no trees. (15)

precious \ 'presh-əs \ Having great worth or value. (140)

presented arms \ prē-'zent-əd àrmz \ Held their rifles upright in front of them while standing at attention, as a salute to show respect. (156)

preserves \ prē-'zərvz \ Whole fruits canned or made into jams or jellies. (232)

preserving \ prē-'zərv-ing \ Keeping from rotting. (190)

Prime Minister \ 'prīm 'min-əst-r \ The chief of the men who help the ruler to govern the country. (91)

professors \ prə-'fes-rz \ Teachers, usually in a college. (25)

protested \ prə-'test-əd \ Objected strongly. (252)

providential \ ˌpräv-ə-'den-chəl \ Because of or coming from God's care; lucky. (291)

puppet \ 'pəp-ət \ A doll moved by rod, hand, or strings. (32)

Puritan \ 'pyù-rə-tən \ A member of a church group that had very plain services and thought that merry-making was wrong. (160)

purpose \ 'pərp-əs \ Plan; aim; something one has in mind to get or do. (119)

Q

quarterdeck \ 'kwort-r-ˌdek \ The upper part of the deck, or floor, at the back of the ship, used by the officers. (74)

R

radiation \ ˌrād-ē-'āsh-n \ The process by which energy, such as heat and light, is given off in rays. (276)

rafter \ 'raft-r \ A long, heavy, slanting piece of wood used to hold up a roof. (117)

rarely \ 'rar-lē \ Not often. (35)

rations \ 'rash-nz \ A daily share of food. (193)

receipt \ rē-'sēt \ A written statement that money has been received. (254)

reckon \ 'rek-n \ To think; to suppose. (238)

recognize \ 'rek-ig-ˌnīz \ To see and know who someone is. (52)

reservations \ ˌrez-r-'vāsh-nz \ Lands set aside for a special purpose. (224)

restore \rē-'stōr\ To bring back. (35)

result \rē-'zəlt\ Outcome; that which happens because of something. (44)

rhythm \'rith̲-m\ Movement in which some action is steadily and evenly repeated. (139)

ridiculous \rə-'dik-yə-ləs\ Absurd; laughable. (37)

Rio Grande \'rē-ō 'grand, 'grand-ē\ A river in the southwestern United States. (13)

rocket \'räk-ət\ An engine in which fuels are burned and changed into hot gases that are forced out through a hole at the bottom, thus moving it forward. (275)

rollicking \'räl-ik-ing\ Frolicsome; gay; merry. (295)

rotates \'rō-ˌtāts\ Turns around as a top or wheel does. (209)

Round Tower \'raund 'taur\ One of many round stone towers with cone-shaped roofs built in olden times to guard against attacks. (147)

S

saddlebag \'sad-l-ˌbag\ A large bag of leather or fabric that hangs from one side of a saddle. (221)

sahuaro \sə-'wä-ˌrō\ A cactus in desert parts of the southwestern United States and Mexico, that grows as high as 60 feet or more, with white flowers and fruit. (218)

samisen \'sam-ə-ˌsen\ An Oriental banjo-like three-stringed musical instrument. (133)

sandalwood \'sand-l-ˌwud\ A sweet-smelling wood from the Asian tree of the same name. (188)

scanty \'skant-ē\ Hardly large enough. (115)

scarlet \'skär-lət\ A bright red color, with some orange. (117)

scoffed \'skȯft\ Mocked. (246)

seven seas \'sev-n 'sēz\ All the waters or oceans of the world. (74)

shift \'shift\ To move from one place to another. (278)

shuttle \'shət-l\ In weaving, a bar which carries the thread from side to side through the threads running up and down. (139)

skeleton \'skel-ət-n\ The framework. (292)

skimmed \'skimd\ Moved quickly and lightly over. (108)

slabs \'slabz\ The rough outside pieces cut from a log. (291)

smocks \'smäks\ Loose coats worn over clothes to protect them from dirt. (100)

smoldering \'smōl-dər-ing\ Burning or smoking without flame. (171)

sod \'säd\ The layer of ground containing the grass and its roots. (167)

Spanish dagger \'span-ish 'dag-r\ A dagger-like plant of the southwestern United States. (14)

spring \'spring\ A small stream of water coming from the earth. (170)

spyglass \'spī͜glas\ An instrument used for viewing faraway objects. (74)

stagbeetle \'stag-͵bēt-l\ A beetle with jaw parts somewhat like a stag's antlers. (30)

stock-still \'stäk-'stil\ Perfectly still. (232)

strained \'strānd\ Used as much as possible. (163)

strait \'strāt\ A narrow waterway between two large bodies of water. (191)

strands \'strandz\ Threads or strings. (136)

sturdy \'stərd-ē\ Strong. (91)

submarine \͵səb-mə-'rēn\ A ship that can go under water. (200)

submerge \səb-'mərj\ To put or sink under water. (96)

sullen \'səl-ən\ Not sociable; silent; gloomy. (297)

sumac \'sü-mak\ A large bush with feather-shaped leaves and pointed bunches of furry, red berries. (161)

surface \'sər-fəs\ Top. (41)

survived \sər-'vīvd\ Were left alive. (196)

suspended \sə-'spend-əd\ Kept from falling or sinking by something unseen. (165)

swayback \'swā-͵bak\ A sagging of the back, or a hollow in the back, especially of horses and donkeys. (220)

T

tattered \'tat-rd\ Torn. (188)

Tea Ceremony \'tē 'ser-ə-͵mō-nē\ In China and Japan, the making and drinking of tea according to old rules and customs. (135)

thatched-roof \'thacht-'rüf\ With a roof made of straw. (80)

thicket \'thik-ət\ A thick growth of bushes or small trees. (48)

thong \'thȯng\ A narrow strip of leather. (301)

tinder \'tind-r\ Something which catches fire very easily; used to start a fire from a tiny spark. (145)

tinder box \'tind-r 'bäks\ A small box for holding tinder, flint, and steel for starting a fire. (145)

tons \'tənz\ Measures of weight, each equal to 2000 pounds. (224)

traces \'trās-əz\ The two straps of a harness that fasten an animal to whatever it is pulling. (41)

tribute \'trib-͵yüt\ Money paid by the ruler of one country to another for peace and protection. (195)

trim \'trim\ Neat and orderly. (112)

triumphantly \trī-'əm-fənt-lē\ Joyfully because of success. (24)

tuft \'təft\ A small bunch of hairs fastened at one end. (48)

turreted \ 'tər-ə-təd \ Standing up like little towers. (116)

tusks \ 'təsks \ Long, greatly enlarged teeth. (91)

type \ 'tīp \ Kind or sort. (86)

U

uranium \ yü-'rā-nē-əm \ A metal which sends out rays of energy that can be used to run an engine. (202)

V

vanilla \ və-'nil-ə \ A climbing plant which has beans used in making vanilla flavoring. (173)

veldt \ 'velt \ A wide stretch of open, grassy land in South Africa. (48)

venturesome \ 'vench-rs-m \ Willing to take chances; bold. (190)

veranda \ və'ran-də \ A porch. (25)

volcano \ väl-'kā-ˌnō \ A mountain having an opening at the top through which steam, ashes, and melted rocks are thrown up. (75)

voyage \ 'vȯi-ij \ A journey by water to a faraway place. (188)

W

warp \ 'wȯrp \ The threads running lengthwise in a piece of cloth. (138)

warthog \ 'wȯrt-ˌhȯg \ A wild hog with large tusks and a rough growth on each cheek. (48)

wash \ 'wȯsh \ The dry bed of a stream that sometimes runs and sometimes does not; often at the bottom of a canyon. (222)

waterbuck \ 'wȯt-r-bək \ A large antelope which lives near rivers and likes to swim. (48)

water line \ 'wȯt-r 'līn \ Line where the surface of the water touches the side of a ship or boat. (94)

weave \ 'wēv \ To make cloth by crossing threads in and out, over and under. (136)

wildcat \ 'wīld-ˌkat \ A fierce, quick-tempered, hard-fighting person. (292)

wildebeest \ 'wil-də-ˌbēst \ A large, thick-set antelope; same as gnu. (48)

wisp \ 'wisp \ A bit or small puff. (171)

wits \ 'wits \ Mind; sense; the power to think. (102)

woeful \ 'wōf-l \ Sad; sorrowing. (118)

wonder drug \ 'wənd-r 'drəg \ A medicine that does amazing things in helping people to get well; a miracle medicine. (266)

woof \ 'wu̇f \ The threads running from side to side in a piece of cloth. (138)

woven \ 'wōv-n \ Made by weaving. (136)

Y

yoke \ 'yōk \ Two animals joined together by a frame of wood fitting over the necks. (41)

READABILITY

Peacock Lane, the Fourth Reader of the *Reading Caravan* series, meets the requirements of fourth-grade readability.

The readability analysis is based on the first six units of the book. Unit 7, the last unit, is set apart for particular emphasis on elements of literary quality—theme, characterization, plot, and style—and is therefore not included in the analysis.

The Dale-Chall *Formula for Predicting Readability* reveals that *Peacock Lane* has a raw score of 4.7. This raw score, when converted according to the Dale-Chall table of estimated corrected grade levels, indicates that the book is at the level of fourth grade or below and is therefore well within the reading ability of fourth-grade children.

There are 721 new words in *Peacock Lane.* The average number of new words per 200 running words is 2.7.

Words assumed to be known are words appearing in the Heath word list, which consists of words common to 5 out of 8 basal readers at the third-grade level or below and 8 out of 8 basal readers at the fourth-grade level; words which appear in the Gates list, *A Reading Vocabulary for the Primary Grades;* and common variants of words from those two lists. Proper names, foreign words, contractions of known words, compounds of known words, parts of known compounds, possessives, nonsense words, syllables representing sounds, and localisms such as *critter* are not counted as new. Many of the words are given special attention in the activities sections and in the glossary. Poetry is not included in the word count.

The changes made in editing or adapting the selections for readability were done carefully so as to keep the author's style. In some cases no changes were made. The selections in Unit 7, the last unit in the book, are reprinted without change.

The illustrations not only enrich and extend the text, but add to its readability.